Heart Disease

About the Authors

Judith A. Skala, RN, PhD, is a Research Instructor in the Department of Psychiatry at Washington University School of Medicine in St. Louis, MO, and an Instructor in Health Behavior and Health Psychology in the Department of Psychology at Washington University. After 20 years of experience in cardiac and psychiatric nursing, Dr. Skala completed the doctoral program in Clinical Health Psychology at Washington University. She was a Research Coordinator of the landmark ENRICHD clinical trial and has been a cognitive behavior therapist for several other clinical trials of treatments for patients with heart disease.

Kenneth E. Freedland, PhD, is a Professor of Psychiatry and Clinical Health Psychology at Washington University School of Medicine in St. Louis. He is an Associate Editor of *Psychosomatic Medicine* and is on the editorial board of *Health Psychology*. His research focuses on the role and treatment of depression and related problems in heart disease. He is a member of the Academy of Behavioral Medicine Research, a Fellow of the Society of Behavioral Medicine, and a Founding Fellow of the Academy of Cognitive Therapy. Dr. Freedland was a CBT supervisor for ENRICHD and has supervised several other clinical trials of CBT for patients with heart disease or other medical illnesses.

Robert M. Carney, PhD, is a Professor of Psychiatry and the Director of the Behavioral Medicine Center at Washington University School of Medicine in St. Louis. Dr. Carney is best known for his pioneering research on the role of depression in coronary heart disease, and he was one of the principal investigators of the ENRICHD clinical trial. He has served on the editorial boards of *Annals of Behavioral Medicine*, *Psychosomatic Medicine*, and *Journal of Consulting and Clinical Psychology*. He has extensive experience as a cognitive behavior therapist and clinical supervisor, and has particular expertise in the treatment of comorbid depression in medically ill patients.

Advances in Psychotherapy – Evidence-Based Practice

Danny Wedding; PhD, MPH, Prof., St. Louis, MO
(Series Editor)
Larry Beutler; PhD, Prof., Palo Alto, CA
Kenneth E. Freedland; PhD, Prof., St. Louis, MO
Linda C. Sobell; PhD, ABPP, Prof., Ft. Lauderdale, FL
David A. Wolfe; PhD, Prof., Toronto
(Associate Editors)

The basic objective of this new series is to provide therapists with practical, evidence-based treatment guidance for the most common disorders seen in clinical practice – and to do so in a "reader-friendly" manner. Each book in the series is both a compact "how-to-do" reference on a particular disorder for use by professional clinicians in their daily work, as well as an ideal educational resource for students and for practice-oriented continuing education.

The most important feature of the books is that they are practical and "reader-friendly": All are structured similarly and all provide a compact and easy-to-follow guide to all aspects that are relevant in real-life practice. Tables, boxed clinical "pearls", marginal notes, and summary boxes assist orientation, while checklists provide tools for use in daily practice.

The series *Advances in Psychotherapy – Evidence-Based Practice* has been developed and is edited with the support of the Society of Clinical Psychology (APA Division 12). The Society is planning a system of home study continuing education courses based on the series that an individual can complete on the web.

Heart Disease

Judith A. Skala
Washington University, St. Louis, MO

Kenneth E. Freedland
Washington University, St. Louis, MO

Robert M. Carney
Washington University, St. Louis, MO

HOGREFE

Library of Congress Cataloging in Publication

is available via the Library of Congress Marc Database under the
LC Control Number 2005928392

Library and Archives Canada Cataloguing in Publication

Skala, Judith A.
    Heart disease / Judith A. Skala, Kenneth E. Freedland, Robert M. Carney.

(Advances in psychotherapy–evidence-based practice)
Includes bibliographical references.
ISBN 0-88937-313-2

    1. Coronary heart disease–Psychological aspects. 2. Congestive heart failure–Psychological
aspects. I. Freedland, Kenneth E. II. Carney, Robert M. III. Title. IV. Series.

RC681.S62 2005   616.1'23'0019   C2005-903582-X

PUBLISHING OFFICES
USA: Hogrefe & Huber Publishers, 875 Massachusetts Avenue, 7th Floor,
                Cambridge, MA 02139
                Phone (866) 823-4726, Fax (617) 354-6875; E-mail info@hhpub.com
EUROPE: Hogrefe & Huber Publishers, Rohnsweg 25, 37085 Göttingen, Germany
                Phone +49 551 49609-0, Fax +49 551 49609-88, E-mail hh@hhpub.com

SALES & DISTRIBUTION
USA: Hogrefe & Huber Publishers, Customer Services Department,
                30 Amberwood Parkway, Ashland, OH 44805
                Phone (800) 228-3749, Fax (419) 281-6883, E-mail custserv@hhpub.com
EUROPE: Hogrefe & Huber Publishers, Rohnsweg 25, 37085 Göttingen, Germany
                Phone +49 551 49609-0, Fax +49 551 49609-88, E-mail hh@hhpub.com

OTHER OFFICES
CANADA: Hogrefe & Huber Publishers, 1543 Bayview Avenue, Toronto, Ontario M4G 3B5
SWITZERLAND: Hogrefe & Huber Publishers, Länggass-Strasse 76, CH-3000 Bern 9

Hogrefe & Huber Publishers
Incorporated and registered in the State of Washington, USA, and in Göttingen, Lower Saxony,
Germany

Printed and bound in the USA
ISBN 0-88937-313-2

Preface

Cardiovascular disease is the most active area of research in behavioral medicine. This research is published across a wide array of journals, making it difficult for busy clinicians to keep up with new developments in the field. Thus, one of the biggest challenges today is translating the latest findings in behavioral cardiology into clinical practice. This volume is intended to make these findings accessible to psychologists, physicians, social workers, nurses, and other professionals who work with cardiac patients. It is also written for trainees who plan to work in medical settings where they will encounter patients with heart disease. It provides recommendations that are grounded both in research and in clinical practice.

Acknowledgments

Over the years, a number of forward-thinking cardiologists have collaborated with us and shared their insights and expertise. We particularly want to thank Michael W. Rich, MD, Allan S. Jaffe, MD, Victor G. Davila-Roman, MD, Edward M. Geltman, MD, and David S. Sheps, MD, MPH. We have also collaborated with many outstanding behavioral scientists. They are too numerous to name them all, but we do want to acknowledge Nancy Frasure-Smith, PhD and Francois Lespérance, MD for their dedication to the field of behavioral cardiology and for helping to bring it to the attention of the medical mainstream.

We have also worked with many outstanding psychotherapists who have shared their clinical perspectives on psychiatric and psychosocial aspects of heart disease. Iris Csik, MSW, LCSW, Patricia K. Hoffman, PhD, and Maria Calsyn, MSW, LCSW, have been particularly helpful in this regard. We also wish to thank Ms. Csik for her careful reading of this manuscript and for her editorial suggestions.

We are grateful for the patient support and assistance of the Series Editor, Danny Wedding, PhD, and of Robert Dimbleby of Hogrefe & Huber. Their guidance and encouragement were invaluable.

Most of all, we wish to thank all the people who have come to us with their hardships, not knowing what to expect of therapy, and have agreed to work with us. They have entrusted us with their stories, their problems, their accomplishments, their fears, and their hopes. They have challenged, amazed, and inspired us. This book is dedicated to them with love, respect, and gratitude.

Judith A. Skala
Kenneth E. Freedland
Robert M. Carney

This work was supported in part by Exploratory/Developmental Research Grant Award No. R21MH052629 from the National Institute of Mental Health.

Table of Contents

1

Description

1.1   Terminology

1.1.1   Heart Disease

Many different terms are used to describe various aspects of heart disease. Some, such as **coronary artery disease** (CAD) and **coronary heart disease** (CHD) are often used interchangeably, while others are quite specific. CHD is an umbrella term for most forms of heart disease, but it does not exist as an International Classification of Diseases (ICD-10) code. The various ICD headings for heart disease can be found in the "Diseases of the Circulatory System" section coded 100 to 199. In order to work effectively with patients with heart disease, it is advisable to have a working knowledge of the following terms (ICD-10 code is given when applicable): **chronic ischemic heart disease** (125), historically called **atherosclerotic heart disease** or ASHD, now commonly referred to as CAD or CHD; **congestive heart failure** or CHF (150); **cardiomyopathy**, often written CMY (142); **angina pectoris** (120), which may be classified as stable, unstable, or with documented vasospasm (120.1); ischemia; **myocardial infarction** or MI (121); coronary valvular disorders, generally classified as **valvular stenosis** or **insufficiency** (134–137); **cardiac arrhythmias**, often more accurately called **dysrhythmias** (147–149); **atherosclerosis** (170); atherogenesis; and **aneurysms** of the heart (125.3). Common procedures include: cardiac catheterization, also called cardiac cath; **percutaneous transluminal coronary angioplasty** or PTCA, which now often includes insertion of one or more **stents**; **coronary artery bypass graft** or CABG surgery; and **pacemaker** insertion and/or insertion of an **automated implantable coronary defibrillator** or AICD.

1.1.2   Psychiatric Disorders and Psychosocial Problems in Heart Disease

Introduction

In this volume, we distinguish between **psychiatric disorders,** as defined by the American Psychiatric Association's Diagnostic and Statistical Manual of Mental Disorders, 4th Edition Text Revision (DSM-IV-TR), and **psychosocial problems,** which comprise a variety of other psychological, interpersonal, and social adjustment difficulties in patients with heart disease. In some instances, the distinction is clear. Type A behavior, for example, may be problematic for patients with heart disease, but it is not a DSM-IV psychiatric disorder.

In other cases, it is not so clear. For example, a patient who has recently had a heart attack may be quite anxious yet not meet the criteria for any of the anxiety disorders listed in DSM-IV. Depending upon the context, we discuss these sorts of problems either as **subsyndromal** forms of psychiatric disorders, or simply as psychosocial problems. Phenomena such as Type A behavior that have no counterpart in DSM-IV will only be referred to as psychosocial problems, not as psychiatric disorders.

Depression

The hallmarks of depression are persistent sadness (**dysphoric mood**) and pervasive loss of interest or pleasure in usual activities (**anhedonia**). In clinically significant depressive disorders, these symptoms are accompanied by other symptoms of depression and by diminished ability to engage in everyday activities (**functional impairment**).

> **Patients with subsyndromal depressive symptoms are at high risk of having a major depressive episode**

The term **subsyndromal depression** has taken on several different meanings. Depending upon the context, it can indicate that the cardinal symptoms of dysphoric mood and/or anhedonia are present but the criteria for a full-fledged DSM-IV depressive disorder are not met. It can also mean that the patient has a depressive disorder that is only in partial remission, whether or not dysphoric mood or anhedonia are among the persistent symptoms. In some instances, the term is used as though it were synonymous with DSM-IV minor depression, but this usage is incorrect.

> **Nondysphoric depression is easily overlooked, as depression is often equated with sadness**

Some patients deny feeling sad despite having other symptoms of depression. This condition has been termed **nondysphoric depression**. In some cases, the patient may simply not be feeling sad but may have other manifestations of depression. In others, he or she may actually feel sad but deny it when asked, perhaps because of personal or cultural biases against expressing emotions or to admitting to feeling sad. This is often encountered when assessing depression in medically ill patients, especially in those who are not seeking treatment for depression.

Some depressed patients present with anger or irritability, either instead of, or in addition to, sadness. Anger and irritability can prevent patients from being aware that their underlying mood is dysphoric. However, it is important not to assume that patients who are angry or irritable are necessarily depressed as well. Anger and irritability can be present for reasons unrelated to sadness or depression.

> **"Depression" can refer to a mood, a symptom, or a syndrome**

If you use the National Library of Medicine's Medline database to search for articles on depression, it helps to know that the Medical Subject Heading (MeSH) keyword "depression" refers to "depressive states, usually of moderate intensity, in contrast with major depression present in neurotic and psychotic disorders." In contrast, the MeSH term "depressive disorder" refers to "an affective disorder manifested by either a dysphoric mood or loss of interest or pleasure in usual activities. The mood disturbance is prominent and relatively persistent." This term encompasses major depression as defined by DSM-IV. However, the MeSH term "depressive disorder, major," does *not* refer to ordinary DSM-IV major depression. Instead, it refers to "marked depression appearing in the involution period and characterized by hallucinations, delusions, paranoia, and agitation." In other words, it pertains to psychotic depression in elderly individuals. This is unquestionably a confusing situation.

To make matters worse, "depression" can also refer to certain medical problems that may have nothing to do with psychiatric depression. The best way to find what you're looking for is to use the MeSH term "depression" when searching Medline for articles on mild forms of psychiatric depression such as subsyndromal depressive symptoms, minor depression, or dysthymia, and to use "depressive disorder" when searching for ones on DSM-IV major depression. Better still, use both terms in their exploded form (exp depression/ OR exp depressive disorder/), as some articles about depression are classified in Medline in ways you might not expect.

Anxiety

Anxiety has three dimensions: **cognitive, affective,** and **physical (somatic)**. Worry is the chief cognitive manifestation of anxiety. **Worrying** refers to a repetitive pattern of apprehensive expectations about potential problems, threats to safety or security, or harmful events that might occur. Whereas medically ill patients who have good reason to worry about their health are said to have **health anxiety**, individuals who worry needlessly about less serious aches and pains are said to have **hypochondriacal concerns**. Worrying about other problems is also common among cardiac patients, particularly about ones that either indirectly result from or are worsened by the patient's medical illness.

> The three dimensions of anxiety often differ in severity

The affective manifestations of anxiety include feeling fearful, ill at ease, restless, keyed up, or on edge. These are the sorts of feelings that people ordinarily experience when something frightening happens. Such feelings normally abate after the frightening experience ends, but "anxiety" implies that they persist even when the source of the fearfulness might not be readily apparent to an external observer. For that matter, it might not even be obvious to the patient.

The physical manifestations of anxiety include muscle tension, nervousness, perspiration, insomnia, fatigue, gastrointestinal symptoms, and cardiovascular symptoms such as **palpitations** or **tachycardia** (rapid heart rate), and chest pain. The cardiovascular symptoms of anxiety often cause concern and confusion among cardiac patients, as well as among their families, caregivers, and physicians. It can be difficult, for example, to differentiate between benign chest pain due to anxiety and unstable angina due to coronary disease. This issue is addressed in greater detail in subsequent sections.

The MeSH terms for anxiety are not quite as confusing as the ones for depression. Use the term "anxiety" to search in Medline for articles concerning "persistent feelings of dread, apprehension, and impending disaster." In other words, use this term for subsyndromal forms of anxiety that fall short of the requirements for a DSM-IV psychiatric disorder. Many cardiac patients who do not meet the criteria for an anxiety disorder are nonetheless very anxious at times. The MeSH term "anxiety disorders" refers to "disorders in which anxiety (persistent feelings of apprehension, tension, or uneasiness) is the predominant disturbance." Use "anxiety disorders" when searching for DSM-IV anxiety disorders such as generalized anxiety disorder or panic disorder.

> Terms for searching for articles about anxiety

Stress

This term has a number of different meanings. It can refer, for example, to a subjective state in which the individual feels pressured, conflicted, or overwhelmed. It can also refer to external pressures, problems, or events that make the individual feel stressed. In this volume, we generally use the terms **stressor**, **stressful event**, or **stressful life event** to refer to the external events and conditions to which patients may be exposed, thereby stimulating physiological arousal and subjective feelings of being stressed. We use **perceived stress** or **mental stress** to refer to subjective experiences that result from exposure to stressors or to stressful events. The terms **stress** and **stress response** are broader in that they encompass not only the cognitive and affective components of stress but the physiological ones as well.

The terms **stress** and **distress** are sometimes used as though they are interchangeable, but they have different connotations when applied to the psychosocial adjustment of medically ill patients. Distress comes in a number of different varieties, and perceived stress is one of them. However, a patient who is distressed might be feeling worried, anxious, sad, or upset for reasons that might be unrelated to perceived stress.

The boundaries between stress and anxiety are somewhat arbitrary. Indeed, DSM-IV includes two "stress disorders" under the broader heading of "anxiety disorders." One is the well known condition, post-traumatic stress disorder (PTSD). The other is its younger and less well known sibling, acute stress disorder. These conditions are defined in section 1.2.2. For now, suffice it to say that some of the symptoms of stress and anxiety are virtually indistinguishable.

"Stress," like "depression," has a number of meanings in the medical literature that are not directly related to psychiatric or psychosocial problems (e.g., stress testing.) The playful staff of the National Library of Medicine have also hidden an assortment of MeSH terms pertaining to psychological stress around their electronic garden. If you want articles about clinically relevant problems associated with stress in humans, your search will probably be more successful if you choose the MeSH term "stress, psychological" as it refers to "stress wherein emotional factors predominate." You might also choose the term "stress disorders, post-traumatic" or "stress disorders, traumatic" if you are seeking studies on PTSD or acute stress disorder.

"Stress," like "depression," has a number of meanings in the medical literature that are not directly related to psychiatric or psychosocial problems.

Stress and anxiety present with similar symptoms

Anger, Hostility, and Irritability

Anger can have adverse effects on the cardiovascular system

Anger is a transient emotion or mood associated with feeling threatened, frustrated, or displeased. **Hostility**, in contrast, refers to a more persistent feeling of opposition and anger towards others. Anger and hostility are not necessarily more common in patients with heart disease than in the rest of the population. However, they can be particularly problematic for cardiac patients because of their adverse cardiovascular effects. A patient who is **irritable** is easily angered, frustrated, or made impatient. Thus, irritability refers to the individual's threshold for experiencing or expressing anger and related feelings. Hostility is a persistent characteristic, considered by some authorities to be a personality trait. Irritability, in contrast, typically refers to a transient tendency or state.

Type A Behavior

The **Type A behavior pattern** (**TABP**) refers to a combination of time urgency and hostility that has been studied extensively in relation to heart disease. The time urgency component includes such characteristics as impatience, punctuality, multi-tasking (i.e., doing several different things at the same time, such as simultaneously studying a report and listening to the news while exercising at a health club), ambitiousness, and a sense of discomfort when there is free time to relax instead of engaging in goal-oriented activities. The hostility component includes frequent expressions of anger, aggressiveness, turbulent interpersonal relationships, harsh judgments about others' behavior, and disbelief in altruism. The time urgency and hostility components are apparent not only verbally but also through psychomotor signs such as tense or angry facial expressions and postures, hurried speech, and sighing in response to frustration. Individuals who lack these characteristics are said to fit the **Type B behavior pattern**.

The term "Type A personality" is sometimes used instead of "Type A behavior," and the MeSH term for this phenomenon is "Type A Personality." However, most of the recent scientific literature refers to this construct as a behavior pattern rather than as a personality trait.

Vital Exhaustion

In the late 1970s, Appels and his colleagues in The Netherlands began to investigate **vital exhaustion**, a condition that includes feelings of physical and mental exhaustion, lack of energy, insomnia, irritability, as well as hopelessness, demoralization, crying, and other depression-like symptoms. Appels found that vital exhaustion is a risk factor for acute myocardial infarction, and that its presence could be an early warning sign of an impending MI in individuals with coronary disease. A number of studies have found strong correlations between vital exhaustion and depression, which is not surprising given the number of overlapping symptoms. Consequently, some authorities have questioned whether depression and vital exhaustion are truly different phenomena rather than different names for the same problem. Nevertheless, there is sustained interest, particularly in Europe but also in North America, in vital exhaustion as a risk factor for myocardial infarction and for other expressions of coronary heart disease.

Low Perceived Social Support (LPSS)

Lack of adequate social support, in one form or another, has been shown to predict psychiatric problems such as depression, as well as mortality in a variety of different populations. Social support is a broad construct that includes such variables as the size and quality of one's social network, the circumstances in which one lives (e.g., alone or with others), the availability of practical assistance, and the extent to which one shares emotional bonds with other people. All of these aspects of social support are important, but only some of them have been shown to predict adverse medical or psychiatric outcomes in cardiac patients. They fall under the heading of what has been called **low perceived social support**. This includes such problems as having (or at least believing one has) no one to confide in, no one with whom to share love and affection, and no one to provide emotional support when confronting difficult challenges or decisions.

LPSS is a risk factor for mortality after acute MI

1.2   Definitions

1.2.1   Heart Disease

Table 1
Heart Disease Terminology and Definitions

Term	Definition
Automatic Implantable Cardioverter Defibrillator (AICD)	Implanted battery powered device with electrodes placed directly on heart muscle; delivers electrical stimulation to disrupt dysrhythmias.
Angina	Symptoms that occur when the heart muscle's demand for oxygenated blood exceeds the available supply. (See ischemia.)
Angina Pectoris	Chest discomfort due to insufficient blood flow to the heart muscle.
Aorta	Large main artery into which heart directly pumps and from which blood flows to all other arteries in the body.
Arrhythmias/ Dysrhythmias	Disruption of the electrical conduction system of the heart resulting in irregular and/or ineffective heart muscle contractions.
Atherogenesis	Formation of the deposits on the inner arterial walls
Atherosclerosis	A condition in which deposits of fat and other material (plaque) are distributed along the inner lining of the arteries, leading to arterial narrowing and decreased blood flow to the target organ.
Atrium, pl. atria	The two upper chambers of the heart that send blood to the ventricles during a heart beat (heart muscle contraction).
Coronary Artery Bypass Graft surgery (CABG)	Surgery to replace diseased coronary arteries with peripheral veins or arteries, thereby re-establishing blood flow to the heart muscle
Cardiac Catheterization	Also coronary angiogram; procedure involving injection of "dye" into the coronary arteries to diagnose coronary artery disease.
Cardiomyopathy	Primary disease of the heart muscle; may be congenital or acquired.
Congestive Heart Failure	A chronic progressive disease in which the heart muscle cannot pump effectively, causing fluid build-up in the lungs and extremities
Coronary arteries	Arteries that supply blood to the heart muscle
Coronary Artery Disease	A disease involving damage to the coronary arteries, leading to arterial narrowing and decreased blood flow.
Heart Aneurysm	Outward bulging of a weakened heart muscle wall, usually involving a ventricle (i.e., ventricular aneurysm).
Heart valve	Flap-like structure between heart chambers to prevent backflow of blood. The heart has 4 valves.
Ischemia	Insufficient blood supply, usually due to obstruction; causes angina.
Myocardial Infarction	Heart attack; death of heart muscle tissue due to complete obstruction of blood flow to the affected area.

Table 1 (continued)

Pacemaker	Implanted battery powered device to electrically initiate heart muscle contractions and/or control heart rate and rhythm
Percutaneous Trans-luminal Coronary Angioplasty (PTCA)	Intra-arterial procedure done to flatten plaques against inner wall of artery to increase blood flow.
Stent	Tubular mesh inserted into artery during PTCA to maintain blood flow; may be coated with drugs that prevent clot formation.
Valvular insufficiency	Failure of the valve to close perfectly, allows backflow of blood.
Valvular Stenosis	Narrowing of the valve opening.
Ventricles	The more muscular, lower chambers of the heart. During contractions the right ventricle sends blood to the lungs while the left ventricle sends oxygenated blood through the aorta to the body.

1.2.2   Psychiatric Disorders in Heart Disease

The following tables outline the DSM-IV-TR criteria for the depressive and anxiety disorders that are frequently comorbid with heart disease. (**Comorbidity** refers to the co-occurrence of two or more conditions or illnesses, such as major depression in a patient with coronary heart disease.) The criteria are abbreviated; consult DSM-IV-TR for complete details and additional information.

Table 2
Symptom Criteria for Depressive Episodes

Major Depressive Episode

A. At least five of the following symptoms have been present nearly every day for at least two weeks; at least one of the symptoms is "1" or "2".
   (1) Dysphoric mood (feeling down, sad, etc.)
   (2) Anhedonia (loss of interest or pleasure in usual activities)
   (3) Significant change in appetite or weight
   (4) Insomnia or hypersomnia
   (5) Psychomotor agitation or retardation
   (6) Fatigue or loss of energy
   (7) Feelings of worthlessness or excessive guilt
   (8) Diminished ability to think, concentrate, or make decisions
   (9) Recurrent suicidal ideation or suicidal behavior

B. These symptoms cause clinically significant distress and/or functional impairment, and they are not due to the direct, physiological effects of a medical illness, medication, or drug of abuse.

Minor Depressive Episode

The criteria for minor and major depression are identical, except that only 2–4 of the above symptoms are present in a minor depressive episode.

Table 3
Dysthymic Disorder

A. Dysphoric mood has been present more days than not for at least 2 years. If there have been any breaks in the dysphoric mood, they have lasted no longer than 2 months at a time.

B. While dysphoric, the individual has also had two or more of these symptoms:
   (1) Poor appetite or overeating
   (2) Insomnia or hypersomnia
   (3) Low energy or fatigue
   (4) Low self-esteem
   (5) Poor concentration or difficulty in making decisions
   (6) Feelings of hopelessness

C. There were no major depressive episodes during the first two years of the mood disturbance. (If there were, the disturbance is classified as a form of major depressive disorder.)

D. The symptoms cause clinically significant distress and/or functional impairment, and they are not due to the direct, physiological effects of a medical illness, medication, or drug of abuse.

Table 4
Panic Disorder

Panic disorder is diagnosed when there have been recurrent, unexpected panic attacks followed by at least one month of persistent fear of having more panic attacks, worry about the implications or consequences of the attacks, or avoidance behavior (i.e., attempts to avoid situations in which panic attacks seem likely to occur.) A panic attack is a discrete period of intense fear or severe anxiety in which at least four of the following symptoms appear abruptly and peak rapidly (i.e., within about 10 minutes.)

   (1) Palpitations, pounding heart beat, or rapid heart rate
   (2) Perspiring
   (3) Trembling or shaking
   (4) Shortness of breath or a sensation of being smothered
   (5) Choking sensations
   (6) Chest pain or discomfort
   (7) Nausea or other forms of gastrointestinal distress
   (8) Feeling dizzy, unsteady, lightheaded, or faint
   (9) Feelings of unreality (derealization) or of detachment from oneself (depersonalization)
   (10) Fear of losing control or going crazy
   (11) Fear of dying
   (12) Numbness or tingling sensations
   (13) Chills or hot flushes

Table 5
Postraumatic Stress Disorder (PTSD)

A. The person has been exposed to one or more traumatic events involving experiencing, witnessing, or being confronted with actual or threatened death or serious injury to self or others, and the person's immediate response involved intense fear, helplessness, horror, and/or agitation.

B. The traumatic event(s) are repeatedly re-experienced via intrusive, distressing memories, dreams, or, in severe cases, hallucinations, illusions, or dissociative flashbacks; or by intense distress when exposed to cues (whether external or internal) that resemble or symbolize the traumatic event(s).

C. Persistent avoidance of, and numbed responsiveness to, anything associated with the trauma via avoidance (e.g., of conversations about the trauma, of places where the events occurred, of memories of the events, etc.), diminished participation in activities, detachment or estrangement from others, restricted emotions, or lowered expectations about the future.

D. Persistent symptoms of physical and/or emotional arousal, as indicated by insomnia, irritability, difficulty concentrating, hypervigilance, or exaggerated startle response.

E. The symptoms have been present for at least one month.

F. The disorder causes significant distress or functional impairment.

Table 6
Acute Stress Disorder

• The criteria for acute stress disorder are very similar to those for PTSD, except that the symptoms are present during the first month following a traumatic event.

• If the symptoms persist more than one month, the diagnosis of PTSD supersedes that of acute stress disorder.

• PTSD is classified as "acute" if the symptoms have been present less than 3 months and as "chronic" once they have persisted at least 3 months. Thus, the terms acute PTSD and Acute Stress Disorder refer to different phases of the same underlying disorder.

1.3 Epidemiology

1.3.1 Heart Disease

The prevalence of coronary artery disease has increased markedly over the past 100 years. Although it accounted for approximately 10% of deaths at the end of the 19th century, this increased to half of all deaths in the developed nations by the end of the 20th century and it is gaining ground in other nations as Western influence spreads. People who have had an MI are 4–6 times more likely to die of sudden cardiac death than are people who have never had an

Deaths from heart disease have increased in the last century

Table 7
US Heart Disease Statistics

UNITED STATES 2002	CHD	CHF	MI
Prevalence	13,000,000 cases 6.9 % of population	4,900,000 cases 2.3 % of population	7,1000,000 cases 3.5 % of population
Total males	8.4 %	2.6 %	5.0 %
Total females	5.6 %	2.1 %	2.3%
Asians	5.0 %		
Black males	7.4 %	3.1 %	24,322
Black females	7.5 %	3.5 %	25,852
Hispanics	4.8 %		
White males	8.9 %		5.1 %
White females	5.4 %		2.4%
Total Mortality	494, 382	52,828 (in 2001)	179,514

Source: American Heart Association: Heart Disease and Stroke Statistics – 2005 Update

MI. Women under 50 are twice as likely to die after a heart attack than men in the same age group.

Ethnic minorities are particularly at risk

In 2001, the rate of premature death (< 65 years) from diseases of the heart was highest among American Indians/Alaskan Natives (36%) and Blacks (31.5%), and lowest among whites (14.7%). Premature death was higher for Hispanics (23.5%) than Non-Hispanics (16.5%), and for males (24%) than females (10%). No data are available for the empty cells in the table.

In Canada, cardiovascular disease is tracked according to physician billing, hospitalizations, termed "hospital separations," and mortality determinations, so Canadian heart disease rates are not directly comparable to those of their neighbors to the south. The latest available Canadian figures are from 1999.

Table 8
Canadian Heart Disease Statistics

CANADA 1999	CHD	CHF	MI
Hospital Separations/100,000	607	200	205
Number of female deaths in 1999 and (% of all deaths)	19,000 (17.9)	2646 (2.5)	8978 (8.5)
Number of male deaths in 1999 and (% of all deaths)	23,617 (20.8)	1845 (1.6)	11,948 (10.5)

Source: Public Health Agency of Canada, Cardiovascular Disease Surveillance On-Line

1.3.2   Psychiatric Disorders in Heart Disease

Depressive Disorders

Most North American studies of depression in patients with a recent history of acute myocardial infarction have reported point prevalences of approximately 15 to 20% for major depression and similar values for minor depression as defined by DSM-IV. Thus, at least 30% of these patients meet the criteria for a depressive disorder. Some studies have used self-report questionnaires such as the Center for Epidemiologic Studies Depression Scale (CES-D) or the Beck Depression Inventory (BDI), rather than standardized diagnostic interviews for DSM-IV disorders, to define the prevalence of depression. These studies tend to report much higher point prevalence estimates for clinically significant depression; some have been as high as 60%. The discrepancy is primarily due to the low specificity of these depression questionnaires; high scores sometimes reflect problems other than depression.

Chronic medical illness is a risk factor for major depression

Since depression is very common in patients with a recent history of acute MI, it is often assumed that these cases of depression are *caused* by the MI. However, between 40% and 50% of patients who are found to have major depression after an acute MI were already depressed at the time of their MI. In some cases, the onset of the depressive episode precedes the MI by anywhere from several weeks to many months. Furthermore, about half of all patients who are found to meet the criteria for major depression after an acute MI have had at least one prior episode of major depression at some point in their lifetime. In the general population, the typical age of onset of first-ever major depressive episodes is in late adolescence or early adulthood. In contrast, acute myocardial infarctions are rare before middle age. In women, acute MI is very uncommon until after menopause. Furthermore, major depression is more common in women than in men, both in the general population and in patients with heart disease. All of this points to the fact that many cardiac patients have problems with depression years or even decades before they ever have an acute MI.

The onset of depression precedes the onset of acute MI in some cases and follows it in others

Depression is almost as common in patients with clinically stable coronary disease as it is in patients who have had a recent acute MI. It is also very common during the first year after coronary bypass surgery. Indeed, some studies suggest that depression may be even more common, and possibly more persistent, after bypass surgery than after acute MI.

Depression also affects many patients with congestive heart failure. For example, we recently studied a large group of patients who had been hospitalized with CHF. Twenty percent of them met the DSM-IV criteria for major depression during the hospitalization, and 16% met the criteria for minor depression. However, the prevalence varied dramatically by age and by the clinical severity of heart failure. The highest prevalence of major depression was found among patients with severe heart failure who were younger than 60. Two out of every three (67%) of these patients had major depression.

Young adults with CHF are especially vulnerable to chronic major depression

Anxiety Disorders

Anxiety is exceedingly common among inpatients, in part because heart disease and its treatment can be highly anxiogenic. However, less is known about anxiety in cardiac patients than about depression. The existing evidence, although limited, suggests that full-fledged DSM-IV anxiety disorders are less common in these patients than is subsyndromal anxiety.

The estimated prevalence of panic disorder in cardiac patients has ranged from as low as about 10% in some studies to as high as 50% in others. Among patients hospitalized for an acute coronary syndrome, the best available estimate is approximately 10 or 11%, and another 5 or 6% meet the DSM-IV criteria for generalized anxiety disorder. In contrast, at least 20% of ACS patients have subsyndromal anxiety.

Panic disorder appears to be especially common among patients who have established heart disease yet whose cardiac-like symptoms cannot be fully explained by their heart condition. It is also very common among patients who do not have heart disease but who believe that they do. Individuals with **non-CAD chest pain** do not have clinically significant coronary disease yet nevertheless experience chest pains that may lead them to believe that they are having a heart attack. Many of those who present for emergency care have panic disorder, and/or other conditions such as functional gastrointestinal disorders that can cause chest pain. However, many patients who do have significant coronary disease, including ones who have had life-threatening myocardial infarctions, also have chest pain for reasons having nothing to do with their heart condition. The inability to differentiate between the symptoms of an impending heart attack and more benign sources of chest pain can itself be highly anxiogenic. However, clinicians should be careful not to assume that chest discomfort is necessarily benign because the patient is anxious.

> **Differentiating between angina and benign chest pain can be difficult for patients with anxiety**

1.4   Course and Prognosis

1.4.1   Heart Disease

The various diseases of the heart have different courses and outcomes. This is made even more complex by the fact that many heart diseases overlap with one another, often in the setting of other comorbid medical illnesses. Depression, anxiety, and other psychological, social, and financial problems add to this complexity. The earliest manifestation of cardiovascular disease, fatty streaks on the inner linings of the arteries, has been observed in children as young as 11 in the United States. Typically, problems related to coronary artery disease begin to appear in men around the age of 45, and in women, about a decade later.

Unfortunately, there is usually no warning that heart disease is developing and most people remain asymptomatic until they have arterial narrowing of about 70%. Once the flow of blood to an area or areas of heart muscle is sufficiently decreased, people often begin to experience symptoms of angina, shortness of breath, weakness, and/or fatigue with increased physical stress. Although many people equate the term *angina* with chest pain, other common anginal symptoms include pressure or burning in the chest, neck, jaws, or throat; pain, numbness, or tingling down the left arm and into the fingers; pallor, sweating, and nausea. Anginal chest pain may be experienced as traveling through the chest into the back, typically between the shoulder blades. It is not unusual for patients to state that they do not have any chest "pain" but to complain of tightness or pressure. Typical statements include, "it felt like an elephant was sitting on my chest," and "it felt like someone was tightening a vise around my chest." In women, angina is often misdiagnosed because it can appear in the form of flu-like symptoms, abdominal fullness or discomfort, or right-sided chest and arm pain. The presence of angina symptoms does not necessarily mean that the individual is having an acute myocardial infarction. Anginal symptoms that *are* associated with an acute MI tend to be more severe, more persistent, and less responsive to treatment with nitroglycerin. However, this is not always the case; in fact, many patients have an **asymptomatic** or **silent** MI.

Although the ECG pattern may show signs of insufficient blood flow or **ischemia** with increased **mental stress**, symptoms are frequently absent or unnoticed. Many people will be tested at this point and may receive medications and/or procedures to treat the symptoms and underlying problems. With treatment and lifestyle changes to decrease risk factors, most people with heart disease live a normal, active life. Indeed, some patients adopt a *more* active lifestyle after they are confronted with heart disease.

For about 50% of those with heart disease, their first-noticed sign of heart disease is a heart attack or MI. An MI is the result of a total blockage to a coronary artery or arteries. In the past, most cardiologists believed that the arteries that put people at greatest risk for total blockage or **occlusion** were those with the greatest degree of **stenosis** or narrowing. More recently, it has been determined that instability of a particular plaque is more predictive of total occlusion. The course of recovery and overall prognosis following MI is related to the extent and location of heart muscle damage. For example, a patient with a large frontal or **anterior** MI has been shown to be at greatest risk for complications, such as ventricular aneurysm (weakening of the muscular wall of the left ventricle) or death. Over a period of about 6 weeks, scar tissue forms over the damaged muscle wall allowing it to withstand the continued stretching of adjacent muscle tissue, and a zone of stunned heart muscle (myocardium) surrounding the damaged area will likely recover.

The term **acute coronary syndrome** has come into common usage to encompass the presentation of *either* MI *or* unstable angina. Angina is considered unstable when it occurs unexpectedly and without provocation at rest, it requires more treatment to end the discomfort, or it is the first episode. The underlying pathophysiology and clinical management of MI and unstable angina are quite similar.

For those with congestive heart failure or CHF, the outlook and treatment is somewhat different. The most common signs of CHF are shortness of breath with exertion and swelling of the lower extremities due to fluid build-up. CHF might occur as a result of uncontrolled high blood pressure or **hypertension**, a large MI, disease of a heart valve, a viral infection, prolonged high alcohol intake, or comorbid illness such as kidney disease. Sometimes, in the case of **idiopathic** CHF, the underlying cause is undetermined. Once the process of CHF has begun, changes occur that temporarily compensate for the heart muscle's declining function, but these changes ultimately lead to further weakening of the muscle. This worsening can usually be slowed with proper treatment, but the only real "cure" for advanced CHF is a heart transplant. CHF predominantly affects elderly individuals. However, patients with viral

Men and women with angina may present with different symptom patterns

Ischemic episodes that are triggered by mental stress tend to be silent

"Acute Coronary Syndrome" refers to myocardial infarction OR unstable angina

or valvular-based CHF are typically young adults who are shocked to discover that they have a disease which is expected to worsen, become debilitating, and ultimately shorten their lives.

It is not uncommon for a person to develop angina, receive treatment of some kind, eventually experience an MI, have a PTCA or CABG, perhaps have another MI at some point, and then develop CHF. This progression contributes to the high prevalence of depression among patients with heart disease. However, many of these patients do *not* develop depression despite having to cope with a seemingly depressing illness.

1.4.2   Course and Prognosis of Psychiatric Disorders in Heart Disease

Depressive Disorders

About half of the patients who meet the DSM-IV criteria for major depression shortly after an acute MI will either remain chronically depressed or will relapse within 12 months. About half of those who initially meet the criteria for minor depression will completely remit within 12 months, but those who do not remit are more likely to progress sooner or later to major depression than to have chronic minor depression or dysthymia.

The majority of patients with heart disease will <u>not</u> have a major depressive episode

The **incidence** of post-MI depression is as important as its **prevalence**, but it has not been studied as extensively. (Prevalence refers to the proportion of the population that has the disorder; incidence concerns the proportion of individuals who are initially free of the disorder but who then go on to develop a new case of it within a specified period of time.) Recent evidence suggests that as many as 30% of patients who were not depressed at the time of their acute MI will go on to develop either minor or major depression within one year, and that the majority of cases develop during the first month.

Post-MI depression can become chronic if left untreated

Among patients whose coronary disease is detected *before* a myocardial infarction or other serious cardiac event has occurred, the one-year course of depression after the initial cardiac diagnosis is similar to that seen in post-MI patients. Approximately half of the patients who have major depression at the time their coronary disease is diagnosed will either remain chronically depressed or relapse within one year, and over 40% of those with minor depression at the time of diagnosis will go on to develop major depression. However, the one-year incidence of depression appears to be substantially lower in this group. Patients who have little if any past history of major depression, and who do not experience a major depressive episode around the time that their coronary disease is diagnosed, are at low risk for major depression during the first year thereafter.

Two recent multicenter clinical trials have given us some of the best available data on the prognosis of post-MI depression. In the Sertaline Antidepressant Heart Attack Randomized Trial (SADHART), post-MI patients with major depression were randomly assigned to receive sertraline (a selective serotonin reuptake inhibitor [SSRI] antidepressant) or placebo for 24 weeks. There was no significant difference between the treatment and placebo groups on the 17-item version of the Hamilton Rating Scale for Depression (HRSD); both groups started with scores of about 20, and both groups dropped about 8 points over the course of the trial. This represents a substantial improvement yet indicates that the average patient still had some depressive symptoms approximately 6 months after entering the trial, whether or not active treatment was provided. There was a larger treatment vs. placebo difference among patients with recurrent major depressive disorder than for those whose first-ever episode of depression occurred around the time of the acute MI, and an even bigger one for those with relatively severe, recurrent major depression. The latter group started the trial with HRSD scores in the mid 20s. The HRSD scores dropped about 12 points in the treatment group compared to only 9 in the placebo group. Again, the average actively-treated patient improved substantially but remained at least mildly depressed by the end of 24 weeks of treatment, and the average placebo-treated patient remained moderately depressed. These findings suggest that rapid and complete remission of post-MI major depression is the exception rather than the rule, even for patients treated with sertraline.

The Enhancing Recovery in Coronary Heart Disease (ENRICHD) clinical trial enrolled post-MI patients who were depressed and/or who had low perceived social support. The depression eligibility criteria permitted enrollment of patients with major depression, minor depression, or dysthymia. All of the participants were randomly assigned to usual care or to an intervention lasting up to 6 months that included cognitive behavior therapy (CBT) and, in some cases, sertraline. The patients who were given sertraline either entered the trial with relatively severe major depression, or failed to show a sufficiently rapid response to CBT. The depressed patients averaged about 18 on the HRSD at enrollment. The HRSD scores dropped 10 points over 6 months among those in the intervention group, compared to about 8 points in the usual care group. Like SADHART, the ENRICHD trial results suggest that complete remission of depression is an elusive outcome in the first 6 months after an acute myocardial infarction. Many patients who have a clinically significant depressive episode around the time of their MI will continue to have subsyndromal depressive symptoms, or even a chronic depressive disorder, for months after the acute hospitalization.

> **ENRICHD and SADHART were the first large clinical trials for depression in post-MI patients**

Anxiety Disorders

There has been relatively little research on the course and prognosis of anxiety disorders in cardiac patients. One recent study found that about 1/3 of ACS patients have clinically significant anxiety. About 50% of these patients continue to experience significant anxiety 6 months later, and about 25% of them are still anxious a year later. Furthermore, about 15% of patients who are only mildly anxious around the time of hospitalization for ACS develop more severe anxiety symptoms within one year.

1.5   Differential Diagnosis

1.5.1   Heart Disease

When heart disease is suspected, a stress test is often done to observe how the heart reacts to physical stress. Usually, a patient is asked to walk on a treadmill while having his/her ECG and blood pressure monitored. Every few minutes, the pace or grade of the treadmill is increased until the patient achieves a pre-specified heart rate/blood pressure, symptoms occur, the heart rate and blood pressure no longer increase in response to increased stress, or the patient declines to continue. **Pharmacological stress tests** with drugs such as dipyridamole are used to induce cardiovascular stress in patients who are unable to exercise due to disability, frailty, or other limitations. Even with the addition of radionuclide scans, physiological stress testing is less reliable for women than for men. Furthermore, **mental stress tests** are sometimes used to study the heart's response to psychological stressors. Tasks such as public speaking, video games, and anger-provoking social interactions have been used as mental stressors in recent studies. Mental stress testing is currently performed for research purposes only, but it might become a clinically useful test in the future.

> **Surprisingly, some patients are uncertain about whether they have had a heart attack**

Currently, the definitive test for coronary disease is **cardiac catheterization**. This exam usually entails having a small tube or catheter inserted into a groin artery and then guided toward the heart. A contrast solution is injected at the take-off point of each of the main arteries. This enables the cardiologist to visualize the coronary arteries and to estimate the degree of stenosis. In some cases, however, heart attacks occur in arteries that are not severely stenosed. This is due to **coronary vasospasm**. Its occurrence is deduced when there is definite heart damage but no blockage is observed on cardiac catheterization. Newer technologies, such as PET scans and cardiac MRIs are being developed, tested, and improved, but cardiac catheterization is still the definitive diagnostic procedure.

Myocardial infarction is usually diagnosed by symptom history, characteristic changes on resting ECG, and blood tests. The most important diagnostic measure derived from blood tests is the patient's **troponin** level. Because these tests are quite accurate, the diagnosis of an MI is more reliable today than it was a few years ago. However, it is still common for patients to be unsure about whether they have actually had a myocardial infarction. On the other hand, some patients will call every episode of angina a heart attack. In most cases, it is useful for a therapist to know the extent of heart disease, in order to better gauge the patient's level of understanding of his or her condition.

CHF is generally diagnosed by signs and symptoms with addition of a chest x-ray showing congestion of the pulmonary veins or the collection of fluid around the lungs. This occurs because blood backs up into the lungs and fluid leaks out of the small vessels when the heart no longer pumps it forward efficiently. The extent of left ventricular dysfunction is often estimated by scan or echocardiogram. The **left ventricular ejection fraction (LVEF)** is a measure of the percent of blood ejected from the left ventricle when the heart contracts. A normal LVEF is greater than 50%. An LVEF in the range of 35–50 is considered mild to moderate dysfunction, and LVEF below 25 is indicative of severe dysfunction. Interestingly, daily functioning has been more closely related to depression status than LVEF in a number of studies.

1.5.2   Psychiatric Disorders in Heart Disease

The key differential diagnostic challenge is to differentiate between **psychiatric comorbidity with a general medical condition** versus **psychiatric dis-**

orders due to a general medical condition or substance. The diagnosis of a comorbid Axis I psychiatric disorder such as major depression in a medically ill patient implies that the Axis I condition is a disorder in its own right, one that is not merely secondary to the medical illness. In order to conclude that an Axis I disorder is *due* to an Axis III general medical condition, the diagnostician must establish that the psychiatric symptoms are due *entirely* to the *direct, physiological effects* of the medical illness. Similarly, the conclusion that an Axis I disorder is due to a medication or other substance also requires the diagnostician to establish a direct, physiological, causal relationship between the medication and the symptoms.

Thus, DSM-IV sets a very high diagnostic threshold for psychiatric disorders due to general medical conditions or medications. This is an appropriate diagnosis, for example, when thyroid disease causes a mood disorder because of its direct, neurohormonal effects on the central nervous system. It is seldom the appropriate diagnosis for psychiatric problems in cardiac patients, even among patients with advanced heart disease and multiple medical comorbidities.

Fatigue, for example, is a common symptom of congestive heart failure, but it is also a common symptom of depression. In such circumstances, DSM-IV requires the diagnostician to give the benefit of the doubt to the psychiatric diagnosis. In other words, count it as a psychiatric symptom, even if its etiology is uncertain. On the other hand, rapid weight gain is also common in congestive heart failure, but it is usually due to **edema** (accumulation of fluid) rather than to the compulsive overeating that is often seen in atypical depression. Since this kind of weight gain is **solely** due to the direct, physiological effects of heart failure, it does not count as a symptom of depression.

> **DSM-IV depressive and anxiety disorders are seldom due solely to the direct physiological effects of heart disease**

Etiological uncertainty also leads to other differential diagnostic challenges. For example, consider a patient who has been hospitalized for an acute myocardial infarction and who has 5 symptoms of major depression. However, one of the symptoms is insomnia, and the patient attributes it to being in the hospital. If this symptom is disallowed, the patient no longer meets the criteria for major depression but instead has minor depression. The symptom probably *should* be disallowed if the patient's inability to sleep is due entirely to the physical conditions of the hospital setting, e.g., if it is noisy or if he or she is repeatedly awakened during the night for medications, blood pressure checks, etc. It probably *should not* be disallowed if the hospital environment is physically conducive to normal sleep but is such a frightening place for the patient that he or she is unable to sleep. Such distinctions are often difficult to make, and it is tempting to summarily dismiss symptoms such as insomnia under such circumstances. It is important to remember, however, that in the DSM-IV framework, you should give the benefit of the doubt to the symptom. Thus, unless you have fairly solid evidence that this patient's insomnia is *not at all* due to depression, the correct diagnosis would be major depression, not minor depression.

What, then, is the correct diagnosis if the patient is discharged from the hospital, goes home, and starts sleeping normally again? Was this a case of major depression that started to remit after the patient went home, or was it a case of minor depression all along? It is hard to tell. On one hand, you should not dismiss a patient's psychiatric symptoms simply because they are "understandable" given his or her current adverse circumstances. On the other hand,

> **Psychiatric symptoms may abate as the patient's condition stabilizes, but they may also persist or worsen over time**

you should be circumspect about reaching firm diagnostic conclusions amidst the confusion and turmoil of an acute medical crisis. In such circumstances, the best approach may be to make a provisional diagnosis and then to re-evaluate the patient after his or her situation has begun to stabilize.

1.6   Comorbidities

1.6.1   Medical Comorbidities in Heart Disease

Common comorbid problems

Very few heart patients are free of other medical illnesses, partly due to the fact that certain other conditions are risk factors for heart disease and partly due to the age at which patients are typically diagnosed with heart disease. Some of the most common of these are diabetes, pulmonary disease such as emphysema or chronic bronchitis, obesity, arthritis, and other chronic pain problems. Stroke is one of the cardiovascular diseases, but as this manual focuses on the psychosocial aspects of heart disease, stroke will be considered in a separate volume.

Patients referred for psychological services after a heart attack or cardiac procedure may consider their other medical problems as complicating factors in their recovery, or as more problematic than their heart ailment. These other conditions may be longstanding and have already had profound effects on mood and daily functioning. They may also limit the patient's ability to accomplish some of the tasks associated with depression treatment, such as behavioral activation or even sustained conversation. It is important to obtain a medical history, including the effects of comorbid illness on prior functioning, and to develop a basic working knowledge of common health problems.

1.6.2   Comorbidity Among Psychiatric Disorders

"Comorbidity" refers to the co-occurrence of two or more psychiatric and/or medical disorders

Comorbidity is the rule rather than the exception among psychiatric disorders. There is overwhelming evidence for this from a number of major epidemiological studies, including the National Comorbidity Survey (NCS) and the more recent NCS Replication. In the replication study, for example, 6.6% of the adults who were surveyed met the DSM-IV criteria for a major depressive episode within the past year. Nearly 65% of these individuals also met the DSM-IV criteria for at least one other psychiatric disorder; about 58% of them had an anxiety disorder and 8% had a substance abuse disorder.

There has been relatively little research on the comorbidity of psychiatric disorders in patients with heart disease. Many cardiac patients with major depression also have clinically significant anxiety, yet only a subset of these patients meet the criteria for panic disorder or generalized anxiety disorder. Consequently, anxiety is often treated as an associated problem in depressed cardiac patients rather than as a separate disorder. Of course, when full-fledged panic disorder or other debilitating anxiety disorders are present, with or without comorbid depression, they require appropriate clinical attention.

2

Theories and Models of the Disorder

2.1   Depression

Depressive disorders are more common among cardiac patients than they are in the general population. However, this association is not limited to heart disease per se. The prevalence of depression is relatively high in most major chronic illnesses. Furthermore, patients with multiple medical illnesses are at higher risk for developing major depression than are those with only one medical condition.

Multiple medical co-morbidities increase the risk of depression

Heart disease is depressogenic in part because of its perceived ramifications. The cognitive-behavioral model posits that it is not the patient's heart disease that causes depression, but rather what he or she thinks and believes about the heart disease and/or its consequences. For many patients, the consequences are much more distressing than is the heart disease itself. It is not unusual, for example, for post-MI patients to not dwell on their heart attack, but to spend a lot of time ruminating about such questions as whether they will ever be able to achieve their goals or live to see their grandchildren.

The cognitive-behavioral model also emphasizes the role that **behavioral deactivation** plays in depression. The specific pattern of behavioral deactivation differs across patients, but it often includes decreases in physical activities, pleasurable activities, and/or activities that promote a sense of mastery, accomplishment, or purpose. Behavioral deactivation can result from depression, but it can also begin for other reasons and then contribute to the development and persistence of a depressive episode.

Depression and inactivity feed each other

In patients with heart disease, the process of deactivation often begins with an unavoidable change in activity patterns, e.g., during the period of convalescence after an acute MI or CABG surgery. However, some patients become deactivated because they have misinterpreted their physician's advice or because they have exaggerated fears about their physical vulnerability. For example, Dr. Robert Lewin and his colleagues in the United Kingdom have found that some patients with coronary disease mistakenly believe that every episode of angina, no matter how mild, is a essentially a small heart attack, and that these episodes eventually add up to cause as much damage as a massive heart attack. The logical conclusion patients draw from this false premise is that it is extremely dangerous to engage in any kind of physical activity that might provoke exertional angina. This is directly contrary to the advice they were probably given by their cardiologist. Cardiac rehabilitation can help patients to overcome such barriers to physical activity, which is one of the reasons why it can have beneficial effects not only on physical recovery but on psychological recovery as well. Unfortunately, depression is itself a common

Mistaken beliefs about heart disease can increase functional impairment and distress

Medical illnesses can overwhelm a patient's coping resources

Table 9
Factors That Increase Vulnerability to Depression in Cardiac Patients

- Female gender
- Relative youth (onset of heart disease in young adulthood)
- Family history of major depression
- Previous episodes of major depression (more episodes → higher risk)
- Multiple stressful life events in recent months and years
- Inadequate social support
- Functional limitations

barrier to participation in cardiac rehabilitation. In short, behavioral deactivation is often a multidisciplinary problem in depressed cardiac patients.

Although distorted thinking and behavioral deactivation often play significant roles in the onset and persistence of depression in cardiac patients, **realistic problems** often do so as well. Medical illness can create a cascade of other problems, such as unemployment, financial difficulties, family role disruptions, and marital discord. It can also arrive in the midst of such problems and make it even more difficult for the patient to cope with them. Thus, relative deficits in problem-solving and coping skills also have an important place in the cognitive-behavioral model of depression in heart disease.

Heart disease may be depressing, but not every patient with heart disease becomes depressed. Some patients with terminal heart failure remain upbeat despite their circumstances, while others with much less serious conditions become depressed. Stressful medical events such as an acute MI are more likely to precipitate depressive episodes in patients who are vulnerable to depression than in those who are more resilient.

Depression can also exacerbate heart disease and worsen some of its consequences. There is strong evidence, for example, that patients who have major depression after an acute MI are as least twice as likely to die over the next year or two as are patients who are not depressed. Patients with milder forms of depression are at a somewhat increased risk as well. As another example, depression is a stronger predictor of functional impairment in patients with congestive heart failure than is the severity of left ventricular dysfunction. Thus, the relationship between heart disease and depression is *reciprocal* rather than unidirectional.

Depression is frequently accompanied by other negative emotions such as anger as well as other psychosocial problems such as low perceived social support and lifestyle behavioral problems such as smoking. Consequently, one must ask whether depression per se has adverse effects on the course and outcome of heart disease, or whether these effects are due to related problems. The current weight of evidence indicates that depression has independent effects on heart disease, above and beyond the effects of related psychosocial and behavioral factors. For example, a Canadian study found that past history of major depression, current symptoms of depression, current symptoms of anxiety, and the severity of heart disease were all independent predictors of recurrent cardiac events in post-MI patients.

As another example, there is strong evidence of an association between smoking and depression: Individuals who smoke are more likely to become

Other risk factors for depression are also increased for patients with heart disease

Dysphoric mood and anger can co-occur; they are not mutually exclusive

depressed, and depressed individuals are more likely to smoke. Smoking is also a well-established risk factor for heart disease. Consequently, most studies of depression as a risk factor for medical morbidity and mortality in cardiac patients have controlled for cigarette smoking. Despite the association between depression and smoking, most of these studies have found depression to be an independent risk factor for adverse cardiac outcomes even after controlling for smoking.

Depression interferes with smoking cessation

Enough evidence about the adverse cardiovascular effects of depression has now accumulated that some cardiologists regard it as a bona fide cardiac risk factor, much like hypertension or hyperlipidemia. However, this is far from universal. Many remain cautious about concluding that depression plays any sort of causal role in heart disease, in large part because the mechanisms underlying this relationship are poorly understood. It is not enough to show that depression predicts medical morbidity and mortality in patients with heart disease; it is also necessary to explain *why* it predicts these outcomes.

The list of candidate mechanisms can be divided into two broad categories, pathophysiological and behavioral. In order to identify pathophysiological mechanisms, researchers have looked for factors that are associated both with depression and with adverse cardiovascular outcomes. Cardiovascular autonomic dysregulation is a good example. Patients with major depression tend to have elevated resting heart rates, and in the context of coronary heart disease, a high heart rate can increase the risk of having an acute MI or a potentially lethal arrhythmia. Thus, one way that depression might negatively affect cardiovascular outcomes is by raising the patient's resting heart rate. Some of the other leading pathophysiological candidates include increased levels in the bloodstream of chemicals such as **C-reactive protein** (CRP) that are associated with inflammation or with blood clotting (**coagulation**).

Depression may affect heart disease via multiple pathways

Candidate behavioral mechanisms linking depression to adverse cardiac outcomes include nonadherence to prescribed medication regimens, and lifestyle risk factors such as smoking and physical inactivity. Depression has been associated with decreased medication adherence in a variety of different medical illnesses, and with smoking and physical inactivity in both physically healthy and medically ill populations. For example, one of our studies investigated whether cardiac patients take their aspirin as prescribed. Since aspirin interferes with the blood's ability to form clots, it is routinely prescribed to patients with coronary disease in order to help prevent them from having an acute MI. The study found a significantly lower rate of adherence to the preventive aspirin regimen among depressed than nondepressed patients.

Antidepressants do not explain the adverse effects of depression on the course of CHD

The distinction between behavioral and pathophysiological mechanisms is an artificial one. To the extent that behavioral mechanisms affect medical outcomes, they probably do so via physiological mechanisms. Returning to the aspirin example, the behavioral act of taking aspirin has no direct bearing on whether a patient with coronary disease is likely to have an acute MI. By taking aspirin, however, the patient increases the "slipperiness" of the platelets in his or her bloodstream. Platelets play a central role in blood clotting and hence in the process of coronary occlusion that causes acute MIs. Ultimately, the explanation for the adverse effects of comorbid depression in heart disease will be found in a comprehensive **biobehavioral model** that integrates the behavioral and pathophysiological effects of depression on the cardiovascular system.

Shared genetic factors might also help to explain the relationship between depression and heart disease

2.2   Anxiety

Heart disease can be highly anxiogenic, as can some of the interventions that are required to treat it. Many patients feel extremely anxious during an acute cardiac event, often because they fear that death may be imminent. Some patients are even more frightened of the prospect of being permanently disabled by a massive MI than they are of dying from it. Since severe anxiety is relatively common under the circumstances, many patients are sedated during emergency treatment for an acute myocardial infarction. However, anxiety management may be less systematic after the patient is stabilized.

Effective treatment of anxiety during acute cardiac events may help to prevent further distress during recovery

In a recent study, patients were asked to complete an anxiety questionnaire within 48 hours of hospital admission for an acute MI, and their hospital records were reviewed to determine whether and how their anxiety was being treated. Less than half of the hospital charts made any mention of whether the patient had been asked about anxiety; patients who were highly anxious (according to the anxiety questionnaire) were no more likely to have been clinically assessed for anxiety than were the less anxious patients. Approximately 25% of the patients were treated pharmacologically for anxiety, and nearly half received some type of minimal nonpharmacological intervention such as reassurance or recommendations to relax. There was little relationship between whether the patient was evaluated for anxiety and whether he or she was treated, and the efficacy of treatment was inconsistently documented. In a little over half of the cases in which the patient had been given an anxiolytic medication, there was a subsequent note concerning whether it appeared to be effective. There was seldom any documentation whatsoever of the efficacy of any of the nonpharmacological interventions.

Decision-making about health care is a common source of anxiety

There are a number of other anxiogenic moments in the course of heart disease as well. It can be fairly frightening, for example, when an apparently healthy middle-aged adult suddenly starts having exertional angina. The definitive diagnostic procedure, cardiac catheterization with coronary angiography, is generally quite safe but there is a small risk that it could trigger an MI or stroke. Patients are usually sedated during the procedure, but if significant coronary disease is detected, they may be confronted shortly thereafter with questions about whether to proceed with an angioplasty or even with coronary bypass surgery. The risks of angioplasty are similar to those for angiography, and it can be anxiogenic for similar reasons. Heart surgery is considerably more anxiogenic. It may or may not be the single most frightening kind of operation that anyone might ever have to face, but it is certainly on the short list.

Many patients gradually adapt to the more anxiogenic symptoms of heart disease, but some do not

Dyspnea (difficult, labored respiration or shortness of breath) can be a source of intense anxiety in patients with congestive heart failure. One cause of dyspnea is the build-up of fluid in the lungs, and for many patients, resting supine makes it worse. Although anxiety is an understandable, and perhaps even an automatic, response to dyspnea, it can exacerbate the shortness of breath and make it harder to endure. Although medical management to reduce or eliminate dyspnea is the most important step in managing this source of anxiety, psychiatric or psychological intervention is also necessary in some cases.

There has been less research on anxiety as a risk factor for cardiac morbidity and mortality than there has on depression, but there is evidence that at least some forms of anxiety may predict cardiac mortality. The evidence is strongest for phobic anxiety, including findings from several large, epidemiological studies. The initial studies starting in the 1990s included only men. One of the most recent reports, was based on a sample of over 72,000 women participating in the landmark Nurses' Health Study. Over a 12-year follow-up, phobic anxiety was associated with an increased risk of death from cardiac causes. On the other hand, a number of other large studies have not found anxiety to have any prognostic importance in patients with CHD. In summary, there is still only equivocal evidence that anxiety is an independent risk factor for cardiac mortality.

2.3   Anger, Hostility, and Type A Behavior

In the mid-1970s the Western Collaborative Group Study reported a prospective association between Type A personality and coronary heart disease. This sparked intense interest in Type A personality and Type A behavior as a cardiac risk factor, and dozens of studies ensued over the next two decades. In contrast to the early studies, later investigations failed to find an adverse association between Type A behavior and CHD outcomes such as acute MI or cardiac death. A recent meta-analysis examined all of the existing prospective studies and found no association between Type A and CHD. The same meta-analysis did find an association between CHD and the hostility component of Type A behavior. However, the effect size was so small that that hostility appears to have no practical importance for cardiac risk stratification or for prevention of heart disease.

> Hostility is widely seen as being the most important Type A characteristic

It is important to recognize, however, that these studies concern the possible long-term risks of a pattern of hostility, not the cardiovascular effects of anger. Although the overall pattern of evidence remains equivocal, a number of recent studies have suggested that anger may have adverse cardiovascular effects. Some of them have found that **angry temperament** or **trait anger** predicts cardiac events such as myocardial infarction or the need for coronary revascularization, particularly among individuals who do not have hypertension. Others have found that the **expression of anger** predicts cardiac events, for example, after coronary angioplasty.

> Hostile beliefs and attitudes lower the anger provocation threshold

Anger can also have acute cardiovascular effects such as raising blood pressure. In one of the most interesting studies, patients with stable coronary artery disease underwent 24 to 48 hours of ambulatory electrocardiographic monitoring with a Holter monitor, and they kept a detailed diary of their activities and moods. Anger was identified as one of the most common, and one of the most potent, triggers of myocardial ischemia during daily activities. Anger-provoking role-plays have also been used in controlled laboratory studies to induce myocardial ischemia in patients with coronary artery disease. Thus, frequent anger might raise the risk of cardiac events in patients with CAD by raising blood pressure, increasing myocardial ischemia, or other cardiovascular processes.

Given these findings, it is necessary to scrutinize the popular notion that anger is like some sort of harmful force that builds up to a dangerously high level of pressure if one keeps it "bottled up inside." Belief in this myth can lead both patients and professionals to mistakenly assume that "holding anger in" is harmful to one's health and that "letting it out" is therefore beneficial. Research on the cardiovascular effects of anger clearly does not support the notion that expression of anger is beneficial for patients with heart disease. This is not to say that it is necessarily any better for a patient's health if he or she tends to feels angry without overtly expressing it. The problem is anger per se and the physiological arousal that is associated with it. From the cognitive-behavioral perspective, people feel angry when they think angry thoughts and hold angry beliefs, and the more anger they express, the angrier they tend to feel. Consequently, cognitive-behavioral interventions for anger emphasize challenging the validity and utility of anger-provoking cognitions; working to replace them with more helpful thoughts, beliefs, and attitudes; and developing better communication and assertiveness skills so that the patient can employ adaptive alternatives to excessive or inappropriate expressions of anger.

2.4   Stress

Emotional or mental stress has both direct and indirect effects in coronary heart disease. It directly contributes to CHD by increasing the risk of cardiac events, and indirectly contributes by promoting other cardiac risk factors.

Psychological stress has well-documented effects on heart rate, blood pressure, and other cardiovascular parameters

For example, there is mounting evidence that stressful life events increase the risk of having a major depressive episode, at least in vulnerable individuals. Major depression, as we have already seen, is a risk factor for morbidity and mortality in patients with coronary heart disease. A recent, highly influential study found that individuals who experience several stressful life events (such as divorce, financial problems, relocation, etc.) over a period of several years are at higher risk for having a major depressive episode than are similar individuals who experience no more than one or two life events. However, the investigators also analyzed blood samples from their subjects and classified them into different groups according to the characteristics of a particular gene. The gene is one that is involved in the regulation of **serotonin**, a neurotransmitter that plays an important role in depression. Among individuals who had experienced several stressful life events, the genetic pattern made a large difference in the risk of developing major depression. This is an example of a **stress-diathesis model**. Stressful life events, by themselves, are not necessarily sufficient to cause depression, and neither is an inherited (genetic) vulnerability to depression. The combination of the two, however, substantially raises the risk of developing major depression.

Stress also has direct effects in coronary heart disease. Indeed, it has two different kinds of effects: acute or short-term, and chronic or long-term. One way to observe the acute cardiovascular effects of mental stress is to study them in the laboratory. For example, in a multicenter study entitled the Psychophysiological Investigations of Myocardial Ischemia (PIMI), patients with documented coronary heart disease were given both physical and mental stress tests. The mental stress testing protocol included public speaking vignettes and a stress-inducing, computer-administered task. Nearly 60% of the patients developed myocardial ischemia during the mental stress test. It should be noted that they were confronted with fairly mild mental stressors; driving home on the freeway after the testing session was probably a more stressful experience for many of the patients. For patients with coronary heart disease, everyday life provides numerous opportunities for mental stress-induced ischemia to occur. Anger and mental stress are also associated with automated implanted cardioverter defibrillator (AICD) discharges.

Mental stress can trigger episodes of myocardial ischemia in patients with coronary disease

Stress can also have much more serious short-term cardiovascular effects than the kind that were studied in PIMI. The worst ones include acute myocardial infarction and sudden cardiac death. For example, a research team investigating the health consequences of a massive 1995 earthquake in Japan found that it triggered a sharp increase in deaths from acute myocardial infarction. The risk appeared to be greatest in the localities in which the highest percentages of houses were completely destroyed. Of course, massive earthquakes and other major natural disasters are not everyday experiences for most of us, yet disasters on a much smaller scale, such as being involved in a traffic accident or witnessing a violent crime, can also be stressful enough to trigger an acute myocardial infarction or even sudden cardiac death in patients with coronary heart disease.

External stressors such as accidents and natural disasters can increase MI attacks and deaths

Chronic stress might also increase the risk of cardiac events over long intervals. For example, a number of studies have investigated the effects of chronic job strain, effort-reward imbalance at work, or other kinds of occupational stressors. Although the evidence is inconsistent, some of these studies have found that persistently high levels of work-related stress may increase the risk of cardiac morbidity and mortality.

Social isolation and lack of social support are risk factors for mortality

2.5   Low Perceived Social Support

Compelling evidence has accumulated since the 1970s that inadequate social support is a risk factor for mortality in patients with heart disease. However, social support is a complex construct and the evidence of adverse health effects is stronger for some of its elements than for others. A recent review of this literature identified five studies that were especially informative. Table 10 briefly summarizes the findings.

Taken together, these studies suggest that emotional support, especially from family, friends, and other important members of one's social network, is protective for patients with heart disease. Conversely, they suggest that social isolation and lack of emotional support can place cardiac patients at increased risk of dying.

It is not clear whether social support has similar protective benefits when it is provided by individuals other than family members or close friends. For example, therapists can be an important source of emotional support during a time of crisis such as when a patient is recovering from an acute MI, but not much is known about whether this has any effect, positive or negative, on the patient's risk of dying. Similarly, support groups can be very helpful for patients with heart disease, but there is little evidence that they decrease the risk of mortality after an acute MI or at any other stage of heart disease.

Like medications, psychosocial interventions can have unintended side effects

Table 10
Selected Studies of Social Support and Mortality

- Low social integration (few family relationships, close friendships, or social activities) among patients with documented CAD more than doubled the risk of dying over the next several years (Brummet et al., 2001).
- In the "Alameda County" study, social isolation increased the risk of dying over a 9-year period by about 2½ fold (Berkman & Syme, 1979).
- Low social support did not directly alter cardiac mortality risk in a cohort of post-MI patients, but it did buffer the effects of depression on mortality; patients who were both depressed and lacking social support were at higher risk of dying during the first year after an acute MI (Frasure-Smith et al., 2000).
- Lack of emotional support was associated with an almost 3-fold higher risk of dying within 6 months among elderly post-MI patients (Berkman et al., 1992).
- Patients who lived alone were at nearly twice the risk of dying in the first few years after an MI than were patients who lived with others (Case et al., 1992).

Furthermore, it is possible that well-intentioned efforts to improve social support might actually do more harm than good under some circumstances. In the Montreal Heart Attack Readjustment Trial (M-HART), for example, patients received a home nursing intervention after hospital discharge that included provision of reassurance and emotional support, among other ingredients. The overall results of the trial were disappointing in that the intervention failed to decrease one-year cardiac mortality and it had relatively little effect on depression or anxiety. Surprisingly, the mortality rates were slightly higher among elderly women who received the intervention than among women in the usual care comparison group. The authors of the study speculated that this seemingly supportive intervention might have repeatedly reminded the women about their heart attack and unintentionally fueled concerns about their medical prognosis. The visits and phone calls might also have created additional distress for women who were involved in dysfunctional marital or family relationships. A more recent analysis of data from M-HART also found that regardless of gender, patients who utilized **repressive coping** were at increased risk.

Research by Dr. Edwin Fisher and his colleagues has shown that social support can also be counterproductive if there is a mismatch between the kind of support that is being provided and the kind that the patient needs. **Nondirective social support** entails accepting the patient's own goals, helping him or her achieve these goals without taking control of the change process, and validating his or her feelings about the problems being confronted and the challenges involved in solving them. **Directive support**, in contrast, involves taking control and telling the patient what to do or how to view his or her situation.

There are times when directive support is not only helpful but necessary. For example, patients may be utterly incapacitated during the first few days and weeks after an acute MI or after CABG surgery. Directive support is essential for most patients during this period. However, as the patient begins to recover and wants to regain his or her former independence, directive support can be perceived as increasingly unwelcome and intrusive. Nondirective support plays a more helpful role during this phase. Thus, it is important to

Social support tends to peak during acute medical crises and wane during recovery

make an effective transition from directive to nondirective support, and to do so at the right time in the course of the patient's recovery.

We recently conducted a secondary analysis of social support data from the ENRICHD study. It revealed yet another surprising circumstance in which social support may not have the benefits one might expect. We examined whether depression and low perceived social support (LPSS) were both independent predictors of recurrent MI and death, and whether there is an interaction between them. We expected that the adverse effects of depression and LPSS would at least be additive and possibly even multiplicative. In other words, we thought that patients with both problems would be at higher risk than patients with just one of these problems, and that those with only one of them would be at higher risk than patients who were neither depressed nor lacking in social support.

We were wrong, at least about the interaction. It turned out that the patients who were at the highest risk of having a recurrent MI or of dying were those who were very depressed despite having excellent social support. Patients with low perceived social support were at higher risk than were those with good social support, but the patients who were at the highest risk had surprisingly good social support. Previous research has shown that social support buffers against the depressogenic effects of stress. Consequently, it is possible that patients who are severely depressed after an acute MI despite excellent social support may have a particularly intractable and/or harmful form of depression. Since this was an unexpected finding, it should be replicated before being taken too seriously. However, it does suggest that clinicians should pay careful attention to cases in which post-MI patients are severely depressed despite having ample social support.

Post-MI patients who remain depressed despite treatment and/or ample social support may be at increased risk for mortality

2.6   Personality Characteristics

Numerous studies have investigated whether particular personality characteristics increase vulnerability to disease or predict a worse course of illness in patients with an established chronic disease. The literature in this area has been inconsistent and controversial. Some of the strongest evidence that personality factors may play a role in CHD comes from Dr. Johan Denollet's work on what he calls the "Type D" personality. Type D is characterized by a combination of negative affectivity (a construct similar to neuroticism) and social inhibition (the tendency to inhibit self-expression in social situations.) Denollet and his colleagues have reported evidence that Type D predicts morbidity and mortality in patients with CHD.

2.7   Relationships Among Psychosocial Risk Factors

Many studies have examined cardiovascular effects of a single psychosocial risk factor without taking others into account. In studies that have examined multiple psychosocial risk factors, the aim has often been to pit these factors

Many cardiac patients have multiple psycho-social and behavioral (lifestyle) risk factors for morbidity and mortality

against one another to determine which one is the "best" predictor. However, each of the factors discussed in this chapter is related in some fashion to every other one. For example: 1) Depressive disorders and anxiety disorders often occur together, and many depressed patients who do not have full-fledged anxiety disorders nevertheless have clinically significant levels of anxiety. 2) In some cases, depressed patients present with more prominent anger and irritability than sadness. 3) Some of the symptoms of vital exhaustion are virtually indistinguishable from symptoms of depression. 4) Neuroticism or negative affectivity are trait-like tendencies to experience negative mood states such as anxiety and depression. 5) Social inhibition can make it difficult to elicit social support and can make social interactions stressful and anxiogenic rather than comforting. 6) Stressful life events increase the risk of major depressive episodes.

Large samples are needed in order to study multiple risk factors. Even larger samples are often required to examine **interactions** among risk factors, such as questions about whether cardiac patients with both depression and low perceived social support are at much higher risk for mortality than are patients with just one of these problems. Unfortunately, few studies of psychosocial factors in heart disease have been large enough to study risk factor interactions or to determine whether multiple psychosocial factors have independent effects.

Recently, however, the results of a very large, international study of psychosocial risk factors (and other potentially modifiable risk factors) for heart disease was published. INTERHEART was a case-control study of over 15,000 patients with a first myocardial infarction and nearly 15,000 age- and sex-matched controls in 52 countries. Data on several psychosocial risk factors were obtained from 11,119 of the patients (73%) and 13,648 (92%) of the controls. The following factors were significantly more common among the patients than the controls and were collectively termed the **psychosocial index**: work stress, stress at home, severe financial stress, stressful life events in the past year, and depression. These differences were found in both men and women, in a variety of different ethnic groups, and in a number of different regions. There were substantial differences among regions on some factors, however. For example, the proportions of patients with depression and with high overall levels of stress were higher in China and Hong Kong than they were in Europe or North America.

INTERHEART found stronger associations between MI and ongoing, rather than occasional, stress at work or home

INTERHEART provided a unique opportunity to study certain risk factor interactions. For example, the investigators found that the association between depression and MI was stronger among individuals who reported experiencing high levels of stress at work or home than among those who reported little or no stress. In addition, the investigators combined the psychosocial factors into a single index and compared it to "lifestyle" risk factors such as poor diet, lack of exercise, and smoking. The effect of the psychosocial index was nearly as strong as that of smoking, and it was stronger than some of the lifestyle risk factors. Many questions remain to be answered about the role of psychosocial factors in heart disease, but the results of INTERHEART leave no doubt that they do play a role, and an important one at that.

3

Diagnosis and Treatment Indications

3.1   Introduction

Whether to begin an evaluation with a focus on medical or psychological problems depends largely on the presentation. A patient may be an "unhappy referral" who believes that his/her medical complaints are not being taken seriously, or he/she may identify himself or herself as primarily having problems with coping or depression.

3.2   Medical History and Diagnosis

In our experience, most medical patients prefer to begin with the more familiar territory of their medical history and diagnoses. Usually any problems with understanding and coping with their medical condition will become clear during this phase of the interview. It is often difficult to obtain a *complete* medical history, because soon after starting to talk about their medical problems, patients switch to talking about the impact of these problems on themselves and their loved ones. Some practitioners are comfortable allowing an interview to weave around a variety of topics while adding notes to different parts of an outline, while others prefer a more structured approach. With either method, it is important to identify patients' major medical diagnoses, their understanding of them, how long these problems have been present, and their predictions about the future impact of their health problems. Clearly, it is also important to obtain a working knowledge of common diagnoses in order to make reasonable judgments about patients' understanding and expectations. In some cases, basic misunderstandings lie at the root of anxiety and depression and a consultation with the patient's physician may be required. If so, it is important to discuss this with the patient, obtain permission, and come to an agreement regarding the limits of disclosure.

When interviewing about psychosocial problems, inquire about the patient's medical problems first

In addition to getting information about illnesses and conditions, it is important to obtain a list of all medications being taken, including over-the-counter drugs, biologicals, and supplements. They may have an impact on symptoms of depression and anxiety, and they may also provide information about additional medical conditions that the patient may have forgotten to mention. It is also important to ascertain whether the patient routinely takes his or her medications as prescribed. For example, a patient presenting with loss of interest, low mood, and fatigue may simply be forgetting or neglecting to take a thyroid supplement.

Assess the patient's understanding of and adherence to medical advice

3.3   Psychological Evaluation

3.3.1   General Guidelines

When working with a distressed heart patient, it is generally most helpful to focus on present difficulties. This does not mean that historical problems are irrelevant, but that historical information is used in the service of treating current problems and improving functioning as quickly as possible. Once depression, anxiety, or other problems have resolved or lessened, patients may choose to address other, more longstanding issues.

Evaluate referred patients' understanding of and attitude toward the referral

Many patients assume that they have been referred for psychological or psychiatric services because they complained too much, because their physician thinks they are "crazy," or because their physician believes that their persistent problems are "all in their head." These assumptions are barriers to forming a therapeutic relationship. Addressing them explicitly and describing them as common, understandable beliefs, is generally successful. Another common therapy-interfering belief is that accepting psychological therapy would connote weakness, particularly if the patient has observed other heart patients who appear to be coping well. A collaborative approach with a problem-solving focus often helps to allay this concern, especially if it is made clear that it is the patient who will be doing the real "work" of getting better.

3.3.2   Psychiatric Disorders

Chronic subsyndromal distress should be evaluated as it may require intervention

The previous chapter listed the DSM-IV diagnostic symptoms of depression and other disorders that are often comorbid with heart disease. Evaluation might seem to be a simple matter of inquiring whether the required symptoms are present. However, in the setting of fatiguing illness(es) and medications that may disrupt sleep and eating patterns, it is sometimes difficult to determine the presence of the disorder. An even more important question is this: given that it is considered quite reasonable to be unhappy about having heart disease, at what point does this normal human reaction become a disorder?

Premorbid functioning is usually difficult to assess during an acute medical crisis

To answer this, it is important to remember that when one is depressed, symptoms such as dysphoria are not experienced as fleeting feelings or hopeless thoughts about one's health, but rather as a discouraging backdrop to one's life or the gloomy substrate on which one may experience short periods of relative well-being. When patients have trouble determining how often or how long they have been feeling sad or have had a decreased ability to enjoy life, it is often helpful to ask when was the last time they recall feeling good or like their usual selves.

Similarly for anxiety, it is again reasonable to feel concerned about one's health and future well-being in the setting of heart disease. Given that it is often hard for a physician to determine whether certain physical symptoms are cardiac in origin, and that patients are instructed to call their doctor when such symptoms occur, self-monitoring for physical sensations is a very common adaptation to heart disease. Careful questioning and observation should reveal the extent of the anxiety as well as the degree to which normal functioning is disrupted. It is also helpful to determine whether the patient believes that the current anxiety is a change from his/her normal state and/or whether there is a history of being viewed as an anxious or worried individual.

In determining whether a patient meets the diagnostic criteria for anxiety and/or depression, DSM-IV requires that enough symptoms are present, but also that they cause distress and/or impair normal functioning. The challenge is then to determine whether the functional impairment is secondary to the psychiatric disorder or the medical problem. In general, both are contributory and it becomes easier to figure out the relative contributions of each as one becomes more experienced in working with a medically ill population. However, referred medical patients rarely report symptoms as readily as do self-referred psychiatric outpatients, and their presentation is typically quite different than that of psychiatric inpatients.

Depression worsens functional impairment in cardiac patients

Along with the frequently-occurring Axis I disorders, comorbid personality and developmental disorders may also be present. Axis II disorders are not always apparent in the first few therapy sessions. If such problems are suspected, a thorough evaluation is advised and treatment planning should be revised based on any changes to the original diagnostic scheme. In some cases, other problems become apparent over time and psychiatric or neuropsychological referral is required for further evaluation and specialized treatment. For example, a particularly fun and interesting patient may begin to show signs of something more serious such as bipolar disorder, or a patient suspected of cognitive slowing due to moderate to severe depression may in fact be developing dementia either from Alzheimer's disease or multi-infarct dementia.

3.3.3   Psychological Problems

In addition to, or instead of, problems such as anxiety and depression, patients often experience problems in coping such as feeling stressed, angry, irritable, and frightened. As discussed previously, these feelings may be part of depression and anxiety disorders or they may occur separately. As is the case with the above DSM-IV disorders, it is important to avoid making assumptions that these feelings are secondary to or even related to having heart disease or to its treatment. For some patients, heart disease is just one more item on a long list of difficulties they have encountered, and it may not even be the most significant one. Indeed, a medical diagnosis may be welcomed as an acceptable reason to get some long-needed respite from overwhelming demands. In other cases, a patient's situation may be such that little respite is possible despite the additional burden of heart disease with the result that stress, anger, and irritability may increase exponentially. When irritability and anger are new manifestations, it is important to determine the extent to which they may be due to physical discomfort, loss of sleep, or unexpressed fears.

Adjustment to heart disease should be viewed in the broader context of the patient's life circumstances

3.3.4   Social/Interpersonal Problems

Heart disease, heart attacks, and heart surgery are experienced by individuals in a social context. Some families with long-standing difficulties may come together and exhibit a period of improved functioning in response to a crisis, while others

During and after hospitalizations, cardiac patients need both practical and emotional support

may virtually disintegrate as the new burden exacerbates numerous underlying problems. For patients, there may be problems with loss of authority or family/ work role making it difficult to accept care and assistance. Alternatively, patients may report feeling that they have been abandoned when they perceive that they are not getting enough care and attention from those around them. It is often said that men take several weeks off from their work, while women return home to laundry and cooking. While we know of no systematic studies of this phenomenon, we have often observed that long-time homemakers tend to find it difficult to allow their husbands to do housework because "they do it all wrong," and men have been near tears watching their wives mow the lawn.

Coping with such changes may be challenging in the best of circumstances, and one can easily imagine how financial pressures, loss of work, medical complications, and other illness in the family all add to the difficulty and complexity of any given family's situation. When dire poverty, substance abuse, and legal problems are also part of the picture, heart disease might be perceived as the least of a patient's problems, and therapeutic decision-making may be experienced as trying to plug numerous holes in a flood wall.

3.3.5   Health Behavior Problems

Given that heart disease is a chronic condition, secondary prevention is vitally important once the diagnosis has been established. Ideally, patients would learn that they have mild atherosclerosis, initiate lifestyle changes for risk factor modification, and prevent the adverse outcomes associated with disease progression. However, despite the best efforts of various medical societies and associations to educate the public, large-scale lifestyle modification remains an elusive goal. Population-based smoking rates have been falling, but unhealthy eating patterns and sedentary habits leading to obesity, hypertension and type II diabetes (the so-called **metabolic syndrome**) are on the rise.

Motivation for change is a prerequisite for long-term success in health behavior modification

Difficulties with making important lifestyle changes may be the reason for referral for therapy or it may be the patient's own stated goal as treatment is initiated. Changing long-standing habits such as smoking, eating patterns, and failure to exercise are rarely accomplished in the time interval allotted to psychotherapy. If successful outcome of therapy is defined as accomplishing such goals, be prepared for frequent failure. On the other hand, problems with medication adherence, getting started on a prescribed exercise regimen, or joining a smoking cessation program can usually be addressed within the context of therapy by exploring cognitive and practical barriers to initiation of change and by implementing basic problem-solving strategies. Lifestyle change is a worthy goal for nearly all heart patients so the patient and therapist must make some decisions about the order in which problems such as depression, anxiety, smoking, and exercise are addressed, as well as what would be the appropriate venue for treatment. Most individuals with heart disease have limited time and energy resources. Consequently, a strategy of "attacking all fronts" would not only be counterproductive, but potentially dangerous as well.

Patients frequently complain that it is overwhelmingly difficult for them to change their lifestyle. Although it is a good strategy to acknowledge the difficulty of the task, it is essential for the therapist to maintain a sense of optimism about each patient's ability to eventually succeed. When health behaviors become a focus of therapy, it is likely that family members have played a significant role in the patient's decision to make it a focus. Similarly, family members may serve as allies, create obstacles, or bear the brunt of blame for any failures as the process unfolds. It is usually helpful to meet patients' significant others and determine whether they can become effective allies in the accomplishment of the goals of treatment, and whether they should be invited into the therapeutic process.

3.4   Prioritizing Problems and Needs

Once a history and initial evaluation has been completed, patients' problems generally become apparent. What also often becomes apparent is that the problems are numerous, complex, and interconnected in a setting of decreased resources. In psychiatry, it is common to think in terms of a patient's psychological or intellectual resources. In health psychology or behavioral medicine, such issues are considered as a matter of course, but the term "resources" often has a more practical meaning, e.g., the number of sessions allowed, physical limitations, competing demands for visits with other health care providers, or the need to follow complicated regimens such as those required for control of diabetes. Therefore, it is necessary to set priorities and establish reasonable goals based on individual differences and needs.

Prioritizing problems is vital in short-term interventions

As is always the case, patient safety is paramount. When working with cardiac patients, suicide may not be as common a risk as avoiding medical follow-up, being too fearful to start an exercise regimen, losing track of medications taken or missed, or poor communication with a physician. Inquiring whether a patient understands his/her medications and is taking them appropriately may not be a usual role for a therapist, but it is the therapist who is likely to have the longest visits with a patient, to establish the kind of rapport that increases the likelihood of honest responses, and to see the patient frequently enough to detect subtle cognitive changes.

Collaboration between patient and therapist is essential

After safety needs are addressed, a problem list can be discussed and priorities set as a collaborative enterprise. This will be covered in more detail in Chapter 4. Cardiac events are often followed by financial upheavals, changes in work and family roles, and rational or irrational expectations of worsening health with a shortened life expectancy. Concerns about these problems are often magnified by anxiety or depression. Similarly, the demands of caring for a heart patient with severe problems or prolonged depression may exacerbate underlying tensions in the family and even lead to disruption and divorce. In such cases, the life crisis often far outweighs the medical crisis, but under such circumstances, self-care may suffer, leading to development of a new medical crisis as a result. It is a good idea to inquire how the patient thinks he or she is doing, both psychologically *and* medically.

Therapists should remain alert to undiagnosed or newly emerging medical problems

3.5   Referral Issues

Therapists who routinely work with cardiac patients gradually develop a good working knowledge of symptoms, disease process, treatments and medications. Those who plan to work in this area will usually expend great effort to acquire a degree of specialized expertise. However, it is crucial to remember that "one doesn't know what one doesn't know," and to refer accordingly.

Therapists are part of a multidisciplinary care team; they should consult and collaborate with other team members as needed

Whenever medical problems arise, e.g. increased shortness of breath or unexplained or worsening chest pain, it is essential to notify the patient's physician. Such decisions tend to be pretty clear. However, it is not unusual for patients to mention a variety of symptoms in the course of a session or ask a therapist's opinion about whether they should call their physician or not. This becomes even more complicated if a goal of therapy is decreased medical anxiety or reduced dependency on medical caregivers. In such cases, collaboration or at least consultation with the patient's physician is essential. For issues related to severe psychiatric disorders, evaluation for psychoactive medication, and psychiatric emergencies such as elevated suicide risk, referral to a psychiatrist is in order. Always be very careful to restrict your therapeutic interventions to those that are within the scope of your license. When in doubt, consult and/or refer.

In addition to medical referrals, there are a number of care providers whose expertise and experience may be very helpful for the patient. Social workers, cardiopulmonary nurses (such as those who work in cardiac rehabilitation), patient care managers, and pastoral counselors are all available for referral or consultation. Additionally, many foundations and agencies offer disease- or problem-specific support groups. A therapist need never feel alone with the task of determining how best to address their patients' medical problems.

4

Treatment

4.1   Methods of Treatment

4.1.1   Introduction

Heart disease creates a variety of problems that only patients who have it encounter. Only someone who has had a heart attack truly knows what it is like to cope with one. On the other hand, these distinctive problems are essentially variants of ones that many people with healthy hearts experience. For example, an individual who has never had a heart attack may still know what it is like to cope with a sudden, unexpected medical crisis. Furthermore, patients with heart disease are susceptible to all of the other problems that plague the rest of humanity. If anything, having a serious medical illness increases the odds of having other kinds of personal, interpersonal, and practical problems.

Thus, psychotherapeutic and psychopharmacological interventions for cardiac patients have a lot in common with interventions for patients with other kinds of medical illnesses, as well as for individuals who are in good physical health. Many of the same kinds of therapies and therapeutic techniques are applicable in all of these contexts. The key questions, then, are how to choose interventions that are likely to be safe and effective, and how to tailor them to the distinctive needs and problems of cardiac patients.

Therapies that were originally developed for medically well individuals are being adapted for use with cardiac patients

Safety is a more salient concern in treating cardiac patients than it is in working with medically well clients. For example, safety considerations prevent physicians from prescribing certain antidepressant medications to post-MI patients. The ones that are considered relatively safe for these patients are often effective, but not always, and it can be difficult to find safe alternatives. Psychotherapy and other nonpharmacological approaches are free of the medical risks associated with antidepressants, yet they may pose some risks of their own for cardiac patients. Consider, for example, a case in which the therapist is helping a cardiac patient to overcome "excessive" anxiety about having another heart attack. How much concern is too much? How little is too little? A patient may find temporary emotional relief in ignoring angina, only to pay a heavy price later. Consequently, it is important to consider not only the potential psychosocial benefits of helping patients to attain therapeutic goals, but also the potential medical implications.

The possibility that counseling or other nonpharmacological interventions could pose medical risks for cardiac patients was not widely recognized until the results of the Montreal Heart Attack Readjustment Trial (M-HART) were published. M-HART was a large, randomized, controlled trial of a multifactorial case management intervention for nonspecific psychological distress. The results were disappointing; the intervention failed to reduce cardiac mortality. Worse still, the mortality rate was *higher* among older women who received the intervention than among those in the control group. This pattern was initially observed in a one-year follow-up, and it was found again in a five-year follow-up. The five-year analysis also revealed that participants in the intervention group who had a **repressive coping style** had significantly worse survival than comparable patients in the control group, regardless of gender. The intervention might have harmed repressive copers by inadvertently increasing rather than decreasing their distress.

The key lesson to be drawn from this outcome is that seemingly harmless psychosocial interventions for cardiac patients are not necessarily risk-free. Furthermore, it is not unusual for patients to become *more* depressed or anxious during the course of a psychotherapeutic intervention, whether or not this has anything to do with the intervention per se. Consequently, it is essential to systematically monitor changes over time in the patient's mood, not only to measure therapeutic progress but also detect any worsening of symptoms that might occur.

Previous chapters have discussed a variety of different psychosocial and psychiatric problems that are often seen in patients with heart disease. Most of the approaches presented in this chapter are applicable to more than one problem, but some treatments are more effective for certain problems than for others. The following table matches the problems that were discussed in Chapter 2 with some of the psychotherapeutic approaches that are often used to treat them.

Table 11
Types of Therapy and Their Targets

Type of therapy	Targets of intervention					
	Depression	Anxiety	Anger & hostility	Stress	Low perceived social support	Health behaviors
Cognitive behavior therapy (CBT)	X	X	X	X	X	X
Interpersonal therapy (IPT)	X				X	
Problem-solving therapy (PST)	X					
Stress management (SM)	X		X	X		
Behavioral interventions (BI)		X				X
Group therapy & support groups	X	X	X	X	X	X

4.1.2   Psychotherapy

Cognitive Behavior Therapy (CBT)

When behavior modification and other behavioral treatment approaches began to emerge in the 1950s and 1960s, patients' thoughts and feelings were considered to be covert phenomena that could not be directly observed or influenced by therapists, no matter how important they seemed to the patients themselves. These interventions focused primarily on overt behaviors and behavioral skills, and on how behaviors are shaped by environmental contingencies. It was widely assumed that improving behavioral skills and changing problematic patterns of overt behavior would, as collateral benefits, indirectly relieve the patients' troubled thoughts and feelings. This philosophy was widely considered essential at the time in order to put behavioral treatments on a sound scientific footing and to set them apart from psychoanalysis and psychodynamic therapies.

In the 1970s and 1980s, a variety of **cognitive**-behavioral approaches were developed and it became more acceptable to explicitly address thoughts, feelings, moods, and emotions. Albert Ellis and Aaron T. Beck are two of the pioneers of this movement. Ellis is the founder of **rational-emotive behavior therapy** (REBT), a highly directive form of psychotherapy in which irrational, self-defeating beliefs and behavior patterns are confronted and the patient is challenged to change them. Beck is the founder of **cognitive therapy** (CT). CT is part of a broader family of interventions that are collectively called **cognitive behavior therapy** (CBT). In this volume, the term CBT is used to refer both to Beck's therapy and to related cognitive-behavioral approaches.

CBT is a **collaborative** rather than a directive form of therapy, but like REBT, it is also designed to help patients identify and change distressing or otherwise problematic thoughts, beliefs, and patterns of behavior. More research has been conducted on CBT than on REBT, or on any other kind of psychotherapy for that matter. CBT has had a far greater impact than any other kind of psychotherapy on how psychiatric and other psychosocial problems are treated in medically ill patients.

CBT has also had a greater impact on the treatment of depression and other psychosocial problems in cardiac patients than any other kind of psychotherapy. In fact, it was selected as the first-line treatment for depression and low perceived social support in the landmark Enhancing Recovery in Coronary Heart Disease (ENRICHD) study.

> **CBT has been used to treat depression and anxiety in CAD, post-MI, and post-CABG patients**

CBT is an *extension* of behavior therapy, not a replacement for it. The behavioral components of CBT are as important, and in some cases more important, than its cognitive components. It incorporates a variety of techniques derived from behavior therapy, and adds quite a few innovative techniques of its own to the therapist's toolkit. However, CBT is much more than a set of techniques. Its hallmark is the **cognitive model**, a framework for understanding the dysfunctional cognitive structures and processes that underlie maladaptive behaviors and emotional distress. CBT also inherited behavior therapy's commitment to empiricism. Consequently, the clinical practice of CBT continually evolves as clinical trials and other relevant studies are published. Behavior therapists and cognitive behavior therapists share the view that an empirical approach to the individual case is one of the keys to therapeutic effectiveness. Each case is an experiment in which data are collected on the patient's problems and progress. If the data reveal a lack of progress, the treatment plan is changed and more data are collected to determine whether the revised intervention is having the intended effects.

The success of this approach depends upon building a trusting, supportive, and collaborative relationship in which the therapist and patient work together to overcome the patient's problems. Therapists can educate their patients about proven cognitive-behavioral techniques for particular problems, and they can use treatment sessions to help them develop the skills necessary to utilize these techniques, but whether they produce any long-lasting benefits depends upon whether the patients actually use them in their daily lives. Furthermore, therapists cannot directly observe their patients' thoughts, beliefs, and feelings, but must instead infer them from verbal and nonverbal behavior.

The therapist's inferences might be right or wrong; the best way to find out is to discuss them with the patient. Unlike more authoritarian forms of psychotherapy, there is no assumption in CBT that the therapist is an omniscient expert on the patient's inner life or on how to solve the patient's problems. To the contrary, cognitive behavior therapists are expected to "follow the data" and not to rely excessively on their own preconceptions. They are also expected to provide therapeutic advice and directive instructions only when necessary, and to rely primarily on Socratic questioning and guided discovery to help patients evaluate and change their own dysfunctional cognitions. Thus, a collaborative relationship is also essential for the success of the cognitive components of CBT.

This is especially important in working with medical patients who are referred for treatment or recruited for clinical trials. Many of them would not seek psychotherapy on their own initiative, and they are very skeptical about it at first. The respectful, collaborative format of CBT and its practical, supportive, progress-oriented approach, makes it more acceptable to such patients than many other forms of psychotherapy.

Cognitive therapy was originally developed by Beck as a treatment for depression, but it has since been extended to the treatment of anxiety, personality disorders, and a variety of other problems. One of the reasons that CBT is helpful for so many different kinds of psychological problems is that the cognitive model addresses the distressing and self-defeating cognitions that underlie all of them.

Several layers of problematic cognitions are examined in CBT, although not all of them are addressed in every case. They include 1) negative automatic thoughts (ATs); 2) conditional assumptions, attitudes, rules, and beliefs; and 3) core beliefs. ATs comprise the most accessible layer. ATs occur throughout our daily lives in the form of a running commentary on our personal experiences, actions, past, and future. Our ATs track fairly closely with our moods, both positive and negative. When we have depressing or anxiogenic ATs, we tend to feel depressed or anxious; conversely, when we're feeling down or upset, our thoughts usually reflect these negative feelings. Depressed patients tend to have negative ATs about themselves, the world around them, and their future; Beck refers to this aspect of depression as the "cognitive triad."

Consider, for example, two different patients who have just been informed by their cardiologist that, "Your cholesterol is a little higher than I'd like it to

---

Measurement and monitoring of progress is integral to CBT

The patient's perception of the therapeutic relationship is a better predictor of treatment outcomes than is the therapist's perception

Beck's Cognitive Triad in depression: negative views of self, others, and the future

be." Upon hearing this news, the first patient automatically thinks, "Well, I'd better do something about that." The other thinks, "No matter what I do, my health just keeps going downhill. I'm probably going to die any day now." The former patient isn't too happy about this development, but he isn't unduly upset about it either. The latter patient feels discouraged and hopeless because of what he is thinking about the news that his doctor just gave him.

This example illustrates one of the central tenets of the cognitive model: we feel distressed not because of the adverse circumstances and events in our lives, but instead because of how we think about them. As the Stoic philosopher Epictetus wrote in 135 A.D., "Men are disturbed, not by things, but by the principles and notions which they form concerning things." This also illustrates that there is often more than one way to think about an adverse event or circumstance. By changing how we think about adversities, we can change how we feel about them.

The cognitive model focuses on how we can think differently about our problems in order to change the associated feelings

Needlessly distressing ATs result from errors in information processing that are referred to as **cognitive distortions**. Black-and-white (all-or-nothing) thinking is one of the most common distortions in depression. The depressed patient in our current example may be thinking in black-and-white terms about his cholesterol: "If I don't have it completely under control, then it's completely out of control, and because of that, I'm doomed." Absolute, judgmental demands in the form of "should" or "must" statements are another type of cognitive distortion that is very common in depression. Our patient may be thinking, "I *should* be able to control my cholesterol – what's wrong with me? I absolutely *must* control it – or else I'm headed for disaster."

During treatment sessions, cognitive behavior therapists teach their patients how to identify and record distressing automatic thoughts. They then give homework assignments in which the patient is asked to write down examples of distressing ATs that occur during the intervals between sessions. As they review these examples together in subsequent sessions, they consider whether the distressing thoughts are accurate or distorted, and if distorted, what kinds of errors they represent. Through this process, the patient learns to identify and correct the cognitive distortions that are shaping the content of his/her distressing thoughts.

Some ATs are distressing, not because they reflect distorted thinking, but because they *accurately* reflect a harsh reality. This is especially important to consider in working with cardiac patients who may be contending not only with truly difficult medical problems but also with other formidable problems that stem from their medical illness, such as disability, financial hardship, or radical changes in their role in the family. It is counterproductive to question the **validity** of distressing thoughts about these types of problems, i.e., to search for cognitive distortions that might be making the situation more distressing than it has to be. In fact, many patients would see this as insensitive and humiliating, and justifiably so. A more effective approach, and one that helps to strengthen rather than to destroy the therapeutic relationship, is to question the **utility** of accurate but repetitive ATs about harsh realities.

CBT examines both the validity and the utility of distressing cognitions

For example, a cardiac patient was living in constant fear of having another heart attack. The therapist said, "A few weeks ago, your doctor told you that you could have another heart attack. We can see from your homework that you've been reminding yourself about that ever since, and doing so many times a day. And when you do, you usually feel anxious. Can you tell me whether thinking about your risk of another heart attack so often helps you in any way?"

The patient responded by saying, "No, it really doesn't help me at all." The therapist then suggested, "Okay, let's come up with some equally true but less upsetting things you can tell yourself whenever you're thinking about having another heart attack." After some discussion, they agreed that one of the best responses to this thought would be, "Just because I *might* have a heart attack some day, that doesn't mean I'm definitely *going* to have one. I'm doing the best I can to prevent it, but if I ever do have another heart attack, I'll worry about it then. In the meantime, I have better things to do with my life than dwell on something bad that might or might not happen." The therapist asked the patient to write this alternative thought on a "coping card," and to recite it whenever he noticed any anxiogenic thoughts about the possibility of another heart attack. The patient tried using the card during the ensuing week and found that it helped him to feel more relaxed.

By obtaining a sample of ATs in various distressing or otherwise problematic situations, the therapist can make some tentative inferences about the patient's underlying beliefs, attitudes, assumptions, and rules. Therapists should remember that these are merely inferences, not proven facts, until and unless they are substantiated by further data and corroborated by the patient. The ultimate aim of this process is to identify and modify the patient's negative **core belief(s)**, the central organizing ideas that people have about themselves, their place in the world, and other people. According to Beck, most negative core beliefs fall into two broad categories: helplessness and unlovability. The former includes such beliefs as "I'm inadequate," "I'm defective," or "I'm a failure." Examples of the latter include "I'm unwanted," "Nobody will ever love me," and "I'm not as good as other people." Negative core beliefs about others tend to reflect the patient's perceived vulnerability to harm or disappointment, e.g., "I can't trust anyone."

Patients can have both positive and negative core beliefs, with negative ones dominating during depressive episodes

Negative core beliefs can be very distressing when they are at the forefront of one's thoughts, and they can make it quite difficult to function. Consequently, we tend to develop intermediate beliefs, assumptions, and rules to counteract our negative core beliefs. Core beliefs seem to the individual to represent **absolute truths**. In contrast, intermediate beliefs are **conditional**, i.e., "if" statements. For example, a patient who holds the core belief that "I'm not good enough to be loved" might develop the intermediate beliefs, "If I achieve outstanding success, then I'll be loved," and "If I don't try harder than everyone else, no one will ever care about me." We also develop **compensatory strategies** to cope with our negative core beliefs and to put our conditional beliefs, assumptions, and rules into practice. This patient might, for example, work relentlessly to become wealthy, believing that this will make him more desirable.

Intermediate beliefs and compensatory strategies can insulate people from their negative core beliefs for long periods of time. However, core beliefs can become much more salient under adverse conditions, and they can be activated by negative mood states. Thus, in some cases, the ATs reported by depressed, anxious, or otherwise distressed patients may be fairly direct expressions of their core beliefs. Nevertheless, relatively few patients are ready to challenge their life-long core beliefs within the first few sessions of CBT. This is particularly true if treatment is initiated in the wake of a medical crisis such as a heart attack. Many patients need to work for weeks or even months on their ATs and other dysfunctional cognitions before they are ready to work on their core beliefs. Furthermore, work on core beliefs and intermediate cognitions can be difficult or even counterproductive for patients with limited capacity for abstract reasoning, acquired neuropsychological deficits, or low educational attainment. In such cases, the cognitive components of CBT may be deemphasized and the behavioral components accentuated.

Dysfunctional thought records (DTRs) and cognitive conceptualization diagrams (CCDs) are invaluable tools for cognitive therapists. The patient uses DTRs or similar homework forms to collect data on his or her distressing automatic thoughts. The therapist then uses CCDs to organize the resulting samples of the patient's ATs so that themes can be identified. These themes are the basis for the therapist's inferences about underlying cognitions, which are also recorded on the CCD. The CCD evolves throughout the course of treatment as the initial conceptualization is confirmed or disconfirmed, and as further data collection reveals additional dysfunctional cognitions. Judith S. Beck's excellent treatment manual, *Cognitive Therapy: Basics and Beyond*, provides detailed instructions and examples of how cognitive conceptualization diagrams are used in CBT.

> **CBT with distressed cardiac patients often begins with behavioral activation or problem-solving rather than with identification of dysfunctional cognitions**

Core beliefs and intermediate cognitions start to develop in childhood and adolescence, at a developmental stage when illness and death typically seem like remote abstractions with no personal relevance. Consequently, when medical illnesses such as heart disease strike decades later, they may violate deeply held beliefs and disrupt key compensatory strategies, or they may reinforce them in ways the patient never anticipated. For example, when our patient who was working desperately to achieve a personal fortune had a debilitating heart attack in his late 30s, it reinforced his belief that, "No one will ever love me because I'm defective." He viewed his heart attack as making him even more defective than before. By forcing him to quit his lucrative but highly stressful career, it also destroyed his main compensatory strategy for coping with his negative core belief, i.e., striving to become very wealthy in order to become more lovable. Although his heart attack precipitated a severe depressive episode, most of his depressogenic cognitions were not about the heart attack per se but rather about the **personal meaning** of the heart attack. It meant to him that he was becoming more rather than less defective, that he would never be successful, and consequently, that he would never be loved.

> **Beliefs that form long before the onset of heart disease can affect how patients cope with it**

This example is typical in that cardiac patients' most depressogenic cognitions are more likely to be about the personal meaning or implications of the medical illness than about the illness itself. The illness and its treatment are more often the foci of **anxiogenic cognitions**. For example, some patients with coronary artery disease feel extremely anxious whenever they have angina. The kinds of automatic thoughts that often drive this kind of anxiety include, "I'm going to have a heart attack," "I'm going to die," or "They're going to have to operate on me." These ideas are often made even more anxiogenic via cognitive distortions such as **catastrophizing**, e.g., "The surgery is going to be horrible and I'll be scarred for life – if I don't die on the operating table!" Such ATs, in turn, may be fueled by underlying dysfunctional beliefs about helplessness or vulnerability.

In addition to its focus on dysfunctional cognitions, CBT incorporates a wide range of behavioral techniques. The applicability of specific techniques varies across disorders and individual patients. **Behavioral activation** and **problem-solving** are two of the most important behavioral components in the cognitive-behavioral treatment of depression.

Increasing participation in cardiac rehab is often one of the aims of behavioral activation for patients with CHD or CHF

Behavioral activation is especially useful because depressed patients tend to be **behaviorally deactivated**. Mildly- to moderately-depressed patients tend to engage in fewer of the activities that ordinarily give them pleasure or a sense of mastery and accomplishment. Patients who are more severely depressed often discontinue ordinary activities of daily living such as housework, shopping, or self care. The systematic behavioral activation techniques utilized in CBT help patients to increase their activity level in general and their pleasure- and mastery-oriented activities in particular.

Behavioral activation is especially useful early in the course of treatment with patients who are too depressed to focus on their dysfunctional cognitions or who present other barriers to the use of cognitive interventions. Behavioral activation directly targets the functional impairment and social withdrawal that is associated with depression, and it often has potent antidepressant effects. On the other hand, it must be applied with due caution when working with cardiac patients. Consider, for example, a retired patient who has been feeling sad and discouraged about being unable to play golf. Until he developed congestive heart failure, it had been his favorite pastime and the activity around which much of his social life revolved. Getting back on the golf course would probably help him to overcome his depression, but would it be safe? This is not a judgment that is within the scope of most therapists' expertise. The patient's physician should be consulted whenever there is any doubt about the safety of a behavioral activation plan.

Problem-solving therapy and CBT teach compatible problem-solving strategies

The problem-solving components of CBT work on several different levels. They help patients to solve problems that are contributing to their emotional distress and develop skills and strategies that they can apply to future difficulties. Heart disease often leads to a cascade of other problems which the patient is poorly equipped to solve or to cope with. Problem-solving interventions can help patients to overcome the distorted belief that their problems are out of control, unmanageable, or hopeless, and guide them towards taking constructive steps to improve their situation.

In order to develop a cognitive-behavioral treatment plan, it is necessary to identify the problems that are contributing to the patient's distress. It is important to examine how these problems are affecting the patient (e.g., by determining whether cognitive distortions are aggravating these problems or making them more distressing for the patient.) It is also important to differentiate between problems that might be overcome via the use of problem-solving strategies, versus ones that may be more intractable and that therefore call for the use of other coping strategies.

For these reasons, problem lists are especially useful tools in CBT. A cognitive-behavioral problem list form is included in the Appendix. The patient's initial problem list may include items that are not amenable to CBT or that would not be particularly helpful to address. Furthermore, patients' initial lists often omit the main problem(s) for which they are being treated, particularly their depression or anxiety. It is all too easy to become mired in subsidiary problems and lose track of primary therapeutic goals such as eliminating the patient's depression. Consequently, the therapist should work with the patient to develop a collaborative problem list, one that both parties agree includes (and is limited to) the highest priority items to be targeted in the intervention. The list can be revised as problems resolve, as new problems emerge, or as the patient's perspective on his or her problems evolves.

Numerous studies on CBT are published every year, but several recent ones are particularly noteworthy. A team of investigators led by Robert J. DeRubeis at the University of Pennsylvania and Steven D. Hollon at Vanderbilt University recently reported the results of a major randomized clinical trial comparing CBT to an antidepressant medication and to a pill placebo for moderate to severe depression. The response rate after 16 weeks of treatment was 58% in both of the active treatment arms; the remission rates were 46% in the antidepressant arm and 40% in the CBT arm. However, there were important differences between the two sites: Vanderbilt had more complex cases but less experienced therapists than Pennsylvania. Although not statistically significant, there was a trend toward superiority of antidepressants over CBT at Vanderbilt and of CBT over antidepressants at Pennsylvania. These findings are at odds with the assumption that antidepressants are substantially more effective than CBT for moderate to severe depression, but they also point to the critical role that the therapist's training and experience plays in cognitive-behavioral interventions for patients with severe depression and other challenging problems.

> **CBT has been evaluated in numerous clinical trials over the past 3 decades**

Relapse prevention is an integral part of CBT for depression, and a number of studies have suggested that depressed patients learn skills in CBT that help them to prevent recurrent depressive episodes. Patients who responded to CBT in the Pennsylvania-Vanderbilt trial were withdrawn from treatment after 16 weeks and compared over a 12-month period to medication responders who were randomly assigned in double-blind fashion either to continue on the anti-depressant or to switch to a pill placebo. The patients who had been treated with CBT were significantly less likely to relapse than were the patients who were switched to placebo (31% vs 76%), and no more likely to relapse than were those who continued taking an antidepressant (47%). This is some of the strongest evidence to date that CBT yields long-term benefits in recurrent major depression.

A team of researchers led by Dr. Martin Keller, Chairman of the Department of Psychiatry and Behavioral Sciences at Brown University, recently tested a variant of CBT for the treatment of chronic depression. The treatment, known as the **cognitive behavioral analysis system of psychotherapy** (CBASP), was developed by Dr. James McCullough, Jr., Professor of Psychiatry and Psychology at Virginia Commonwealth University. The core intervention in CBASP, and the one that most clearly distinguishes it from standard CBT as well as from standard interpersonal therapy (IPT), is **situational analysis** (SA). The patient is asked to keep track of interpersonally stressful encounters and to record 1) their thoughts and behaviors during these events; 2) whether the outcome of the event differed from the one that the patient had wanted; and 3) why it did not turn out the way the patient might have hoped. Using this method, patients begin to recognize their own roles in shaping the problematic interpersonal situations that have been contributing to their depression. The

> **CBT teaches self-therapy skills as part of a systematic approach to relapse**

focus of the intervention eventually turns toward helping the patient to change his or her behavior in such situations in order to narrow the gap between desired and actual outcomes.

CBASP was compared to the antidepressant nefazodone, alone and in combination, in a large randomized clinical trial. The response rates were 52% for CBASP alone, 55% for nefazodone alone, and 85% for combination therapy. As expected, the complete remission rates were substantially lower than the response rates, but they were impressive nevertheless. This finding is especially encouraging because most of the patients had been chronically depressed despite having tried other treatments. CBASP is an important new addition to the family of cognitive-behavioral treatments for depression. Nefazodone is contraindicated for many patients with heart disease, but CBASP can also be combined with sertraline or other antidepressants that are considered relatively safe for cardiac patients.

Recent studies have demonstrated the efficacy of CBT for a number of other disorders as well. For example, an intervention combining CBT with medications was recently tested in a large, randomized, controlled clinical trial of treatment for panic disorder in primary care patients. The intervention was significantly more effective than usual care.

Cognitive-behavioral interventions have also been developed for a number of different problems in cardiac patients. Over 2,400 patients recovering from a recent acute MI were enrolled in the ENRICHD clinical trial. The participants, all of whom had depression, low perceived social support (LPSS), or both, were randomly assigned to usual care or to CBT. Rapid responders completed the intervention in as little as 6 sessions, but patients received up to 6 months of treatment if necessary. Also, patients who were severely depressed at enrollment, or who did not respond rapidly enough to CBT, were also treated with sertraline. The treated patients had significantly lower depression scores and significantly higher social support scores at 6 months compared to the usual care participants.

CBT was initiated in ENRICHD soon after the MI, but many patients needed more time to recover before they could fully participate in the therapy

Although this was a successful outcome, the results of ENRICHD were disappointing because the intervention was expected to reduce the risks of recurrent MI and death, and it failed to do so. Also, the treated group did have significantly better depression and social support outcomes than the usual care group, but these effects were relatively modest. A recent secondary analysis revealed that the **number of CBT components actually delivered** was one of the strongest predictors of favorable depression outcomes in the treatment group. In other words, the depressed patients who were exposed to the full array of cognitive-behavioral techniques (e.g., behavioral activation, problem-solving, and modification of distressing cognitions) had the most favorable outcomes; those who were exposed to only one or two of these components did less well, on average.

Another secondary analysis of the ENRICHD trial examined late mortality (i.e., deaths occurring no sooner than 6 months after the heart attack) among patients with recurrent major depression. This analysis showed that the patients who responded to CBT (plus antidepressants in many cases) were less likely to die than were patients who either failed to improve or whose depression actually worsened despite up to 6 months of treatment. This underscores the critical importance of monitoring progress during CBT for depression in cardiac patients. Failure to improve may heighten the risk of mortality in these patients. The following table lists steps that cognitive behavior therapists should consider when a depressed cardiac patient is failing to improve.

Table 12
Action Plan for Depressed Cardiac Patients Who Are Not Responding to CBT

1. Elicit patient feedback to identify any unrecognized problems with the treatment plan or with the therapeutic relationship, and adjust accordingly.

2. Assess whether any treatment-interfering cognitions or behaviors may be limiting progress; if so, make them high priority targets of the intervention.

3. Ensure that the treatment plan incorporates the full array of cognitive-behavioral treatment components that are likely to be helpful for this patient.

4. Recommend antidepressant therapy to the patient and, when appropriate, to his or her physician; if the patient is already taking an antidepressant, discuss possible options such as dosage adjustments, augmentation, and/or switching.

5. With the patient's permission, advise the primary care physician and/or cardiologist that more intensive medical management may be needed.

The initial CBT treatment plan should aim for a discernible improvement in mood within the first few sessions

Systematic, session-by-session assessments should be conducted in order to determine whether a patient is improving during CBT or whether his or her symptoms are worsening. Although they are usually not the only goals of treatment, decreasing depression and/or anxiety are often the primary ones when cardiac patients are referred for psychotherapy. For cognitive behavior therapists, the two most important measures for monitoring change are the Beck Depression Inventory (BDI-2) and the Beck Anxiety Inventory (BAI). Both questionnaires consist of 21 items, and each item is rated on a $0 - 3$ scale. Consequently, possible scores on both questionnaires range from 0 to 63.

When using the BDI-2 to assess patients who have been diagnosed with major depression, use the following cut scores: $0–13$ = minimal, $14–19$ = mild, $20–28$ = moderate, and $29–63$ = severe depression. In Beck's original study of the BDI-2, the scores were approximately 29 ± 12 in recurrent major depression, 28 ± 12 in single-episode major depression, 24 ± 12 in dysthymia, and 23 ± 10 in minor depression. Nondepressed patients with anxiety disorders averaged 19 ± 11 and patients with adjustment disorders averaged 17 ± 12. Depressed patients tend to score higher on the BDI-2 than the BDI-1, and the more depressed they are, the larger the gap is likely to be. The difference is about 2–3 points in mild depression and around 3–6 points in more severe depression.

Graph the weekly BDI-2 and BAI scores; review the graph with the patient to highlight progress or to address barriers to improvement

Concerns are often raised about the validity of the BDI's somatic items when assessing depression in cardiac patients or in patients with other medical illnesses. It is unquestionably true that medical illnesses can increase ratings on some of these items in ways that may have little to do with depression. For example, nondepressed patients with severe congestive heart failure tend to score high on the "fatigue" item, simply because fatigue is such a prominent symptom of CHF. However, the BDI was administered to thousands of post-MI patients for the ENRICHD study. When we analyzed the resulting data, we found that the somatic items on the BDI were valid and informative. For example, scores on the somatic items correlate much more strongly with other measures of depression than they do with measures of the severity of heart disease. Furthermore, excluding the somatic items due to concerns about their validity paradoxically decreases the reliability and validity of the BDI when assessing cardiac patients. We recommend administering the entire questionnaire to cardiac patients, both when screening for depression and when measuring weekly progress in CBT.

On average, somatic item scores are higher in depressed or anxious cardiac patients than in nondistressed patients with equally severe heart disease

In Beck et al.'s original study of the Beck Anxiety Inventory, psychiatric outpatients with anxiety disorders averaged about 25 ± 12 on the BAI, compared to around 13 ± 8 among patients with a depressive disorder but no anxiety disorder. According to the BAI manual, a score of 16 or higher is consistent with moderate to severe anxiety. As with the BDI, some of the items on the BAI assess symptoms that may reflect heart disease, anxiety, or both. For example, one of the items asks about whether the patient's heart has been racing or pounding. A patient with an arrhythmia might score high on this item, whether or not he or she was feeling anxious. On the other hand, many patients with arrhythmias *are* anxious, and in some cases, the anxiety is *due to* the arrhythmia. Once again, scores on items that are confounded with the patient's heart disease or other medical conditions should not be ignored. Further assessment is needed to differentiate between the contributions of anxiety and medical illness to these symptoms.

The BDI-2 and BAI should be administered immediately before each CBT session. They should be scored immediately, and discussed with the patient during the session as part of a standard "mood check" item on the agenda. Changes in mood can alert the therapist to items that should be considered for the session agenda and to newly-emerging emotional crises that might necessitate a deviation from the current treatment plan.

Cognitive-behavioral interventions can help patients cope with their heart disease and its treatment

Besides ENRICHD, others recent studies have examined cognitive-behavioral interventions for a variety of other common problems in cardiac patients. For example, Professor Robert Lewin and his colleagues at the University of York in England have developed innovative cognitive-behavioral programs for patients with angina and for patients with an automated implanted cardioverter defibrillator (AICD). In a recent randomized trial, the angina program not only reduced anxiety and depression, but it also reduced the frequency of anginal episodes, increased physical activity, and decreased the need for anti-anginal medication. A recent pilot study of the 12-week AICD program showed that it can significantly improve psychological and functional adaptation to living with the AICD device.

Investigators in the United States have begun testing similar interventions. For example, Dr. Matthew Burg and his colleagues at Yale University have shown in a series of studies that emotional stress and anger can precipitate ventricular arrhythmias in patients with AICDs, and they are developing cognitive-behavioral treatment strategies to address this problem. Dr. Marie Cowan, Dean of the School of Nursing at UCLA, and her colleagues recently tested an 11-session cognitive-behavioral stress management intervention for survivors of sudden cardiac arrest. The results were striking: the risk of all-cause mortality was reduced by over 60% in the intervention group, and the risk of cardiovascular death was reduced by over 80%. This was a relatively small study (n=129), so it should be replicated before any firm conclusions are reached about the ability of the intervention to reduce the risk of mortality. However, the findings are promising.

Dr. James Blumenthal and his colleagues at Duke University recently reported the results of a controlled trial for patients with stable ischemic heart disease. The participants were randomly assigned to supervised aerobic exercise, a cognitive-behavioral stress management intervention, or to usual care. At the end of the treatment phase, participants in both of the intervention groups had significantly lower depression and distress scores, and they had improved significantly on several cardiovascular risk markers.

Our research team at Washington University School of Medicine has also been working on cognitive-behavioral interventions for cardiac patients. Several years ago, we conducted a study in which depressed patients with stable ischemic heart disease were treated with CBT. The treated patients had significant reductions in depression, as assessed by the Beck Depression Inventory, and significant improvements in several indicators of cardiovascular risk. We are currently completing a randomized trial of CBT for depression in patients recovering from coronary artery bypass graft surgery, and another one for patients with congestive heart failure. The intervention for the surgical patients was relatively brief (12 weeks.) In contrast, the heart failure patients received up to 6 months of CBT. The duration of treatment differed in part because the medical course differs between these two patient populations: Most patients gradually recover after coronary bypass surgery, but heart failure is a chronic, progressive condition with a poor long-term prognosis. The final results of both studies are still pending, but our preliminary analyses suggest that the majority of patients benefited substantially from these cognitive-behavioral interventions.

With proper medical supervision, behavioral activation can be used to promote aerobic exercise in cardiac patients

Interpersonal Psychotherapy (IPT)

Aside from CBT, more research has been conducted on IPT for depression than for any other form of psychotherapy. IPT has also been used to treat a number of other problems such as anxiety and eating disorders, but it is most widely used as a treatment for depression. IPT was developed in the early 1980s by Drs. Gerald Klerman and Myrna Weissman. Their approach grew out of prior work by a number of authors, including Adolph Meyer, Harry Stack Sullivan, and others, that focused on the important roles that social and interpersonal factors play in depression. IPT was initially designed to be a short-term, individual psychotherapeutic intervention typically lasting 12–16 sessions. However, it has since been used in other modalities such as dyadic marital therapy, and it has been stretched beyond 16 sessions in some applications and condensed to fewer than 12 in others.

Although social and interpersonal factors are heavily emphasized in IPT, the intervention begins with more of a psychoeducational focus. Interpersonal therapists initially work to educate their patients about depression and its treatment, reassure them about the prospects for improvement and recovery, and advise them about how to manage their depression and its consequences while they are working to overcome it. They may also use a relatively directive approach to help the patient solve discouraging problems. These initial steps help to solidify the therapeutic relationship, reduce the skepticism and hopelessness than many patients feel at first, and increase the patient's willingness to cooperate with the intervention.

The core interpersonal aspects of IPT address social-interpersonal stressors and losses that may have precipitated the depressive episode or that may be maintaining it, and filling gaps in the patient's social support system. In addition, the patient's social-interpersonal role functioning is a key target of treatment in IPT. This helps to break the vicious cycle in which depression impairs social role functioning in ways that drive people away and further disrupts the patient's social support system. IPT therapists are trained to assess and intervene in four domains of interpersonal problems that are common in depression: interpersonal deficits, role disputes, role transitions, and grief. Depending upon the needs of the individual, the intervention may aim to help the patient accept irretrievable losses; repair damaged relationships with family, friends, co-workers, and others; or initiate new relationships.

The efficacy of IPT has been established in several randomized clinical trials of outpatients with major depression. The initial study compared 12 weeks of IPT to amitriptyline and to supportive psychotherapy, as well as to combined IPT + amitriptyline. IPT was superior to supportive therapy and comparable to amitriptyline, and although the effect was not statistically significant, there was a trend toward better outcomes in the group that received combination therapy. Studies that have compared IPT to other antidepressants or to other types of psychotherapy have also provided support for the efficacy of this treatment for major depression.

There has been less research on applications of IPT to cardiac patient populations than there has for CBT. One of the most important studies to date is currently underway in Canada. Drs. Nancy Frasure-Smith, Francois Lespérance, and their colleagues are currently conducting a randomized, controlled clinical trial comparing IPT to citalopram for depressed cardiac patients. They recently reported the results of a preliminary, open-label trial of IPT for 17 patients with stable coronary artery disease and major depression. Ten of the patients received antidepressant medication in addition to IPT. Over 50% of the patients met the study criteria for remission of depression after 12 weeks of treatment.

The Treatment of Depression Collaborative Research Program (TDCRP), a randomized, multicenter clinical trial sponsored by the National Institute of Mental Health, compared 16 weeks of IPT, CBT, imipramine plus clinical management, and pill placebo plus clinical management for patients with major depression. The primary results showed that the severity of depressive symptoms decreased more rapidly among patients who were randomized to imipramine, but by 16 weeks, the effects of IPT, CBT, and imipramine were not statistically different. However, there was a trend toward superiority of imipramine over both of the psychotherapies.

Numerous secondary analyses have been conducted on the TDCRP data. Some of them examined whether IPT or CBT were efficacious for patients with relatively severe depression. This was an important question given prior evidence suggesting that more severely depressed patients tend to respond better to antidepressants than to psychotherapy. The most methodologically sophisticated analysis of the relationship of depression severity to TDCRP outcomes was conducted by Dr. Irene Elkin and her colleagues. They reported than there were no significant between-treatment differences in short-term outcomes among mildly depressed patients (i.e., patients who scored under 20 at baseline on the Hamilton Rating Scale for Depression.) Among the more severely depressed patients, however, imipramine was superior to CBT and to pill placebo, but it was not superior to IPT. There was a trend toward superiority of IPT over CBT, but it was not statistically significant. Furthermore, neither IPT nor CBT were significantly superior to pill placebo. Needless to say, these findings created something of an earthquake in the IPT and CBT communities, and they motivated further research on the question of whether CBT is efficacious for severe depression. (The answer appears to be "yes," according to the recent collaborative study by DeRubeis, Hollon, and colleagues.)

Other secondary TDCRP analyses examined longer-term outcomes. Follow-up evaluations were conducted 6, 12, and 18 months after the end of treatment. The percentage of patients who recovered from major depression and then remained nondepressed during the follow-up did not differ significantly among the four groups. However, approximately 1/3 of the patients who had initially responded to IPT or CBT relapsed, and 50% of the imipramine responders relapsed. The authors concluded that 16 weeks of treatment is insufficient for most patients with major depression to achieve both full recovery and lasting remission. This is an especially important finding as the duration of depression treatment in many clinical trials has been *less* than 16 weeks, not more. Furthermore, it is difficult to obtain approval in many clinical practice settings to provide more than 16 weeks of IPT or CBT, and lengthy courses of psychotherapy are often more expensive than treatment with generic antidepressant medications. Both interpersonal and cognitive-behavioral psychotherapists should strive to achieve rapid progress with their depressed patients, but also implement a relapse prevention plan and provide maintenance-phase therapy if possible.

Finally, a variety of secondary TDCRP analyses have examined predictors of response to treatment. Some of the more interesting findings pertain to differential predictors of outcomes in IPT vs CBT. Given the interpersonal focus of IPT, it was widely expected that patients with high levels of social dysfunction would respond especially well to IPT. Similarly, given CBT's emphasis on modification of distressing cognitions, it was assumed that patients with relatively dysfunctional attitudes would respond favorably to CBT. In fact, just the opposite was found. Low social dysfunction predicted a superior response to IPT, and low cognitive dysfunction predicted a superior response to CBT!

This finding surprised many of us, but in hindsight, it was probably predictable. Most psychotherapists, including practitioners of IPT or CBT, are trained to identify and target the patient's most distressing problems and deficits. This makes obvious sense in some respects. However, it often means that we are highlighting the patient's **weaknesses** and **limitations**, and doing so at a time when he or she is already distressed. Worse still, it can mean that we are depending on the patient's weaknesses and deficits, rather than on his or her strengths and skills, to make therapeutic progress. For example, some depressed patients have little social support because they are socially anxious or lack social skills. Gaining more social support might help them overcome their depression, yet reaching out to others is exceedingly difficult for them. Should their interpersonal therapists expect social outreach to be a particularly fruitful avenue to pursue, especially early in the course of therapy with a severely depressed patient? Probably not. Similarly, patients who score high on measures of dysfunctional cognitions such as the Dysfunctional Attitudes Scale (DAS) tend to have deeply-held, long-established depressogenic or anxiogenic beliefs that may be resistant to change. A cognitive behavior therapist who targets these beliefs as a way to decrease the patient's depression may see little progress as a result.

Patient anger is an important consideration in adapting CBT and IPT to individual needs; angry patients tend to resist therapist directiveness

Thus, it is at least as important to assess and capitalize on the patient's **strengths** and **skills** as it is to identify and target problems and deficits. Furthermore, it is important to recognize that in both IPT and CBT, therapists have considerable latitude to tailor their treatment to the needs of the individual patient. In IPT, the therapist can focus initially on the social-interpersonal domain in which the patient has the best chance of making beneficial changes. In CBT, the therapist has considerable flexibility. If strongly-held dysfunctional attitudes are contributing to a patient's depression, for example, the therapist might defer cognitive restructuring until later in the course of therapy and focus first on problem-solving or behavioral activation. By working with their patients' strengths and resources rather than overlooking them, therapists can achieve better outcomes, particularly in relatively difficult cases.

Stress Management Therapy

Ancient medical texts from China, India, Mesopotamia, and elsewhere proposed that physical health is greatly affected by one's state of mind or disposition. Ancient Greek texts identified certain personality types as being precursors to specific medical illnesses. In medieval Europe, illness came to be viewed as divine punishment for sinful behaviors or character flaws. These views of humanity were holistic in that personality, behavioral factors, and health were considered to be interrelated. In the 1600s, Descartes developed his thesis that humans have a dual nature: a mind which is the realm of the spirit, and a separate, mechanistic body. Although Descartes hoped to settle questions about the nature of human existence, his logic led instead to unsettling questions with which we continue to wrestle.

It has taken centuries to return to a more holistic view of the nature of health and well-being, and research on stress and adaptation has been helpful in this regard. Stress, generally defined as an imbalance between perceived demands from the environment and one's perceived ability to cope with such demands, has been shown to affect health through many pathways, such as the autonomic nervous system, the endocrine system, and behavior.

Brief stress management interventions are provided to patients in some but not all cardiac rehab programs

Now that psychological stress has been shown, in a variety of research contexts, to affect many aspects of health, including immunity and chronic disease processes, what evidence-based treatments are available? Stress management therapy addresses problems through three general approaches: those that focus on stress-related cognitions, those that more directly affect physiological processes, and those that address the external sources of stress, or **stressors**. The various approaches can be used in combination and can be delivered in individual or group therapy formats, as well as in a didactic psychoeducational format.

A cognitive approach begins with a thorough assessment of the thoughts that precede and co-occur when one is feeling stressed. As explained in the foregoing section on CBT, the anxiety-provoking or stress-related thoughts are examined for inaccuracies. Then predictions about negative outcomes and one's inability to cope are tested through a variety of behavioral assignments, beginning with very simple and mildly stressful situations. Throughout this process, patients are trained to utilize more accurate, supportive, coping thoughts which may be written on cards and read frequently to more quickly incorporate the new ideas, or read when under stress and having a difficult time replacing stressful cognitions with adaptive ones. It is important that the coping thoughts address the aspects of the thoughts and beliefs that are responsible for the stress reaction and that they be accurate. For example, it is not particularly helpful to have patients merely repeat to themselves that they can prevail or that things aren't as bad as they seem. Rather, it is more helpful to acknowledge that a situation may be difficult or demanding, but it is unrealistic to expect to be able to do all things well or even to be able to do all of the things one is asked to do. Coping thoughts might also address physiological responses and reinterpret them as normal physical variations. When working with cardiac patients, it is critical to help the patient differentiate between symptoms related to cardiac emergencies and those that are signs of stress or anxiety. This may be difficult or even a bit scary, but patients frequently discern the differences in symptoms and can safely try relaxation techniques and self-talk first, if given the strong admonition to seek medical help if they are unsure of the nature of their symptoms. Consultation with the patient's cardiologist may be necessary with some patients.

Acquisition of stress management skills may help to prevent depression

A more direct approach to physiological stress responses may be used alone or in combination with cognitive therapy. Although biofeedback equipment may be used to help patients learn to reduce muscle tension, biofeedback has not been shown to be significantly more efficient than training guided by simply observing heart rate, respiratory rate, and perceived tension. The patient is best served by developing skills that can be used in vivo in his or her usual environment. Therefore, when training patients in relaxation techniques, it is often better to help them "tune out" noises, lights, and momentary discomforts than to provide a quiet environment that is particularly conducive to relaxation. One begins with breathing awareness followed by breathing control in terms of rate and depth and abdominal rise and fall with each slow breath. After breathing techniques, muscle relaxation is taught. In progressive muscle relaxation (PMR), patients are guided through tensing and relaxing 16 muscle groups. The 16 groups are subsequently combined into eight muscle groups, and then into four. Some authors have claimed that better reduction in muscle tension is achieved if one works only on relaxation without first tensing the muscles, while others claim that the muscle tensing leads to greater awareness of the effect and a stronger sense of control. The muscle tension phase of PMR is contraindicated for patients with painful conditions such as arthritis and for patients with poorly controlled hypertension. The approach for most other patients is to offer both techniques and allow the patient to decide which works best after some practice and experimentation. Successful training leads to the ability to achieve a relaxation effect within a few breaths in most environments.

The goal of PMR and other forms of relaxation training is to enable the patient to relax in stressful situations, not only in peaceful environments

The approach that addresses environmental stressors may include assessment of the situation and the incorporation of straightforward problem-solving. More often, more complex or protracted problem-solving and behavioral changes are required, in conjunction with changes in thoughts, attitudes and beliefs. In some cases, the root problem is only discovered after a thorough examination of the patient's circumstances. Sometimes, a major lifestyle adjustment, such as a change in employment, may be appropriate. When using problem-solving techniques, it is important to differentiate between minor irritations and problems worthy of the investment of the time and effort that may be required for successful solution. Then the patient can do some "brain-storming" during and between sessions without pre-judging any of the possible solutions. Once a list of possibilities is created, these may be examined further for pros and cons until a few reasonable ideas are ready for trial. Of course, not all problems are solvable; ways to improve coping with difficult environments or circumstances should also be explored.

Behavioral Interventions

Behavioral interventions play an important role in modifying cardiovascular risk factors such as smoking and physical inactivity

According to Joseph Wolpe, the term "**behavior therapy**" originated with B.F. Skinner and Ogden Lindsley in 1954, and was brought into wide acceptance by Hans Eysenck. An organizing principle of behavior therapy is that emotional difficulties result from persistent maladaptive behavior patterns that have been learned through explicit instruction, through shaping by environmental contingencies, or both. Just as maladaptive patterns can be learned, they can also be extinguished and replaced by more adaptive behaviors. Another important tenet of behavior therapy is that the therapeutic process should be guided by the principles of experimentation. Strict behaviorists view thinking as a form of behavior and question the utility of considering cognitions as distinct from other behaviors. In 2005, however, the members of the Association for the Advancement of Behavior Therapy (AABT) voted by a four-to-one margin to change the name of the organization to the Association for Behavioral and Cognitive Therapies (ABCT).

When working with heart patients, there are a number of specific situations for which behavioral interventions are particularly well-suited. They include risk factor modification, adherence to treatment regimens, appropriate reactions to perceived symptoms, and adjustments to activity levels. In each case, the success of the intervention is directly related to the accuracy of the behavioral assessment in terms of the antecedents and consequences of the target behaviors. In the behavioral paradigm, for example, anxious thoughts about recommended behaviors are treated as behavioral antecedents that make follow-through less likely.

To combine some of these situations, let's consider nonadherence to a physician's advice to attend cardiac rehabilitation for eight weeks of exercise, social support, and instruction. A patient may be fearful of the consequences of exercise, concerned about the time commitment, shy about interacting with strangers, concerned about body image, or lacking energy or drive due to depression. How one approaches the problem depends on the source of nonadherence.

In one case seen recently, a formerly energetic woman who had worked full-time and cared for a grandchild was extremely reticent to attend cardiac rehabilitation due to fatigue, weakness, shortness of breath with exertion, and depression. Because of her difficulties with mild physical exertion, she perceived increased exercise as potentially dangerous, and she had fallen into the habit of avoiding others because of her depression. She agreed to start with very brief behavioral assignments to do chores such as sitting and folding clothes, to call one friend on the phone, and to limit the length of her daily naps. Whenever increases in her activity level were attempted, she developed symptoms and appeared quite pale. She saw her physician, who adjusted her medications and repeated her advice to the patient to attend cardiac rehabilitation. Thus, a number of different factors contributing to her nonadherence had to be addressed.

Since avoidance precludes opportunities to learn that new activities may be tolerable or even enjoyable, the patient was asked to try one or two sessions as an experiment. She was seen on the day that she was supposed to attend her first session, for which transportation had been arranged. Her therapist sensed her reticence and stayed until she actually got on the bus. The therapist also called the cardiac rehab nurses, with the patient's permission, and warned them about the level of her anxiety. The nurses were very careful to allow the patient to remain in control of her sessions and even suggested that she spend the first session doing preparatory paperwork and watching others. This gave her the confidence that she would not be pushed to do things that she felt were beyond her abilities. By the third session, she noticed some improvement in her stamina, and by the fifth session she looked forward to her thrice-weekly visits. Soon she agreed to follow through with assignments to socialize with friends she had not seen for months. Within two months, instead of retiring, she returned to work while maintaining social activities on a schedule that also allowed for plenty of rest. She later told her therapist that she would have canceled her ride to cardiac rehab had the therapist not been there, and she would have likely retired and stayed in her apartment alone. She had been pushed to exercise for months by various others, but she had resisted. This changed when her therapist instituted a new strategy to help her regain a sense of control and self-efficacy for making her own health decisions.

Problem-Solving Therapy

Problem-solving therapy has been tested with some success as a stand-alone intervention for depression. Some might argue that problem-solving should instead be a facet of a more general approach to brief therapy that focuses on distressing problems. In either case, cognitive and behavioral techniques both apply. The difference is that patients are taught in problem-solving therapy

---

Table 13
Components of Problem-Solving Therapy (Nezu et al.)

1. How one perceives, conceptualizes and approaches (or avoids) problems

2. How to formulate a problem in concrete terms and generate specific achievable goals

3. How to develop a comprehensive and exhaustive list of possible solutions

4. How to weigh alternative solutions in terms of pros and cons to choose the most appropriate strategy to try.

5. How to implement the solution and evaluate its effectiveness.

Brief PST and more intensive CBT can be implemented sequentially in a "stepped care" protocol

how to improve their ability to resolve problems, and the focus remains on specific problems until solutions are found and implemented. For heart patients, problems may be very practical, such as difficulties getting to office visits or being unable to afford medications, or they may be more cognitive or emotional, such as being fearful of returning to work or feeling distant from a spouse who may be perceived as controlling or uncaring. In the setting of a life-threatening illness and/or multiple illnesses, and with comorbid depression and anxiety, even those with fairly good premorbid problem-solving skills often become overwhelmed and perceive their problems as insoluble or themselves as less competent.

Problem-solving therapy teaches patients that when their efforts to solve a problem are initially unsuccessful, they should analyze their approach and either adjust it or discard it in favor of a better alternative. If the patient is having difficulty maintaining the motivation necessary to try successive alternate solutions in the face of discouraging problems, this can be treated as just one more problem to solve. When faced with problems that are essentially insoluble, the focus of therapy becomes the problem of how to make the most of one's life in the face of such adversity. This is a skill which many people with heart disease have shown an amazing ability to develop and maintain.

Motivational Interviewing

Motivational Interviewing is not useful for patients who are already motivated to change

Motivational Interviewing (MI) was developed by William Miller and Stephen Rollnick as a method for facilitating change, initially in the field of addiction treatment. It provided an alternative to some of the confrontational methods that were being promoted in the 1970s and 80s. Miller and Rollnick's excellent text, **"Motivational Interviewing: Preparing People for Change"** (2002), provides comprehensive instruction and a review of applications and research. Its usefulness has been established in the treatment of addictions, in work with repeat offenders, and with several chronic illnesses populations. MI has not been shown to be useful in instances when low motivation is not a factor. It is not a system of psychotherapy per se, but an approach that can be integrated into other therapies and into educational programs for individuals, couples, families, and groups.

MI is based on theories and research about how and why people change their ideas and behaviors. In our culture, it is widely believed that people usually change because they are forced to by dire consequences, by controlling elements outside themselves, or by circumstances or confrontations that spark sudden insights. Therapies, treatments, and punishments based on such beliefs have proven largely ineffective in bringing about lasting change, if any positive change occurs at all. MI rests on the premise that change occurs from within when the individual realizes that change is desirable, feels confident in his or her ability to change, and places a higher priority on change than on the perceived barriers. When these factors come together in the course of one's life, change naturally occurs. When any of these elements is missing, the response is generally one of ambivalence. Thus, when any these factors is absent, motivational interviewing seeks to assist the individual to achieve a state of decreased ambivalence and greater readiness for change. It does this by helping him or her to examine reasons for and against changing, by supporting self efficacy, and by clarifying his or her priorities.

Although MI provides a number of motivation-building techniques, its most important element is its fundamental underlying philosophy, which is exemplified by three dictates: The therapeutic relationship is collaborative in nature, motivation is drawn out or *elicited* rather than instilled, and the client or patient retains autonomy and is ultimately responsible for his/her own decision to change. Miller and Rollnick also outline four general principles of motivational interviewing: 1) express empathy, 2) develop discrepancy, 3) roll with resistance, and 4) support self-efficacy.

Most therapists are familiar with the techniques of reflective listening and accurate empathy that were espoused by Carl Rogers. They convey acceptance of the individual and an understanding that the individual's choices make sense from his or her own point of view. This approach to counseling is essential to the process of motivational interviewing. One might use all of the tools and techniques generally employed in MI, but if the relationship is not based upon acceptance of the client and of the idea that ambivalence is normal, one is not expressing empathy and is therefore not doing motivational interviewing.

The MI technique of developing discrepancy is somewhat more difficult to grasp. Like Linehan's dialectical behavior therapy, MI does not equate acceptance with a lack of drive or desire for change. Rather, its focus is on positive change. It is essentially directive in assisting the client to elucidate the discrepancy between current behaviors and his or her values and ultimate goals in life. It may be that a client is aware of the discrepancy between his or her values and behaviors, but feels ambivalent about instituting change. Through careful questioning and skillful reflective responses, the practitioner of MI clarifies the client's values and amplifies the discrepancy in order to maximize the importance of the change, thus helping him or her to overcome ambivalence and inertia. Throughout this task, it is essential to elicit from the client his or her *own* values and goals as well as reasons for and against change. Two important mistakes to avoid are presenting reasons for change to the client which can then be argued against, and pressuring the client to accept externally imposed goals or values.

Rolling with resistance refers to the stance taken by the counselor that is not only non-confrontational but that actually avoids arguments. Miller advises therapists to stop whatever they are doing if resistance emerges, because it is a signal that the current approach is not working for this client. One might then reframe the client's response and enlarge upon it, agree to some extent but add new information, take the client's side of the issue and allow him or her to provide counter-arguments, or emphasize the client's control over the choices that are ultimately made.

In using each of the above principles, the counselor's goal is to elicit what Miller calls "change talk." This includes anything a client or patient might say that supports change, such as giving reasons for change, identifying actions he or she might be willing to try, forecasting potential benefits of change, or engaging in constructive problem-solving. This serves to highlight the importance of change for the individual.

Change talk might also take the form of statements like, "I guess I could at least try …" This brings us to the last of the four principles: supporting self efficacy. A counselor can only be effective in promoting self-efficacy for making a particular change if he or she actually believes in the client's intrinsic

For patients who are initially reluctant to cooperate with treatment, MI can help to increase readiness for change

MI can help to elicit "change talk" from patients who express self-defeating, pessimistic attitudes about their capacity for behavior change

ability to effect positive change. This goes hand-in-hand with the belief that the client is ultimately responsibility for choosing change and for making it happen. Pep-talk statements like, "I believe in you," or "I know you can do it," not only fall far short of enhancing a client's belief in the possibility of change, but may actually invoke argument to the contrary. Self-efficacy is promoted in many different ways, such as treating clients with respect, accepting their right to change or to choose not to change, accepting their timetable for change, and resisting the desire to provide solutions to problems. Instead, clients are invited to come up with solutions or even first steps toward a solution. Efforts are treated with respect whether success is achieved or not. Self-confidence is assessed along with self-efficacy, and confidence talk is supported in the same way as change talk.

Motivational interviewing seems simple in some respects. Certain aspects of it are in fact basic enough to impart to caregivers in the form of rules to follow or techniques to use when working with patients. However, it is a much more complex and sophisticated approach than this brief review can cover in detail. MI is a fairly new approach, and we expect more refinements and applications to emerge in the coming years.

Crisis Management

Crisis management therapy is similar to problem-solving in that the intervention is brief and focused on a single problem or finite set of problems. It has been successfully used to assist families with recent diagnosis of a major illness, particularly cancer. In this case, however, the problems are more extraordinary and a solution, in the truest sense of the word, may not be possible. For example, a patient who is not a candidate for transplant, may have been informed that her congestive heart failure has progressed to the point that little can be done to alleviate her symptoms or prolong her life. The emotional and practical impact of such information varies widely across patients according to their personalities and circumstances, but it almost always constitutes a crisis. Possible targets of intervention include practical and financial issues, accomplishing meaningful goals, resolving interpersonal issues, talking with family members about the news, exploring spirituality, and reviewing one's accomplishments, to name just a few. In some cases, the direct recipients of the therapeutic intervention are family members rather than the heart patient himself or herself; the patient may be ready to end a long and arduous struggle before his or her family is prepared to accept the inevitable outcome of the illness.

Medical crisis interventions are often designed primarily for the patient's family rather than for the patient

In addition to acute crises, the burdens of chronic illness may reach a crisis point because of the constancy of facing one problem after another, often with few supports in place. Although friends and family frequently provide short-term assistance, at some point their support waivers as they face the competing demands of events in their own lives and in the lives of other loved ones. Some authors believe that this kind of counseling requires specialized training. **Medical Crisis Counseling** by Irene Pollin and Susan Baird Kanaan is a useful reference for therapists who are frequently involved in medical crises.

Group Therapies

Group therapies for heart patients have been shown to be useful in treating stress, anger, hostility, depression, and anxiety. There are also well-established support groups for heart surgery, heart transplant, congestive heart failure, and AICD patients. Support groups often engage guest speakers and provide time for discussion and socialization.

Compared to support groups, therapy groups tend to be smaller, to have more specific therapeutic goals, and to be led by mental health professionals. In order to develop a therapy group, it is advisable to spend a good deal of time in preparation. After working with heart patients for a number of years, recognition of their common and unique problems is inescapable. It may appear that getting people with like concerns together, serving decaffeinated coffee, and allowing them to talk and ask questions is a worthy goal in itself. However, a successful group intervention that actually helps people move beyond prob-

Peer support is one of the most important ingredients in group interventions for medically ill patients

---

Table 14
Planning Group Therapy Services for Cardiac Patients

1. Learn all you can about other successful groups and about your patients' perceptions of what they need and want. Numerous books are available about group therapies as well as published articles describing tested interventions.

2. Determine the group population: e.g., depressed MI patients, AICD patients, or CHF patients
   Who might be inappropriate for this group?

3. Determine the overall goals of the group:
   What do you want the participants to learn?
   What skills do you want them to develop?
   What do you hope they will get from the group process?
   What areas might be beyond the scope of this group?
   Does the structure allow for participants to set some of the goals?

4. Consider your resources:
   Is there institutional support?
   Is there a safe and accessible meeting space?
   Will it be necessary to charge a fee or ask for donations?
   Will fundraising or sponsorship be needed?

5. Determine the structure or format of the group:
   How frequently will the group meet? (Consider issues such as the patients' stamina, functional limitations, transportation, and other barriers.)
   Open or closed groups? (Open groups require stand-alone outlines for each session.)
   One group leader or a team?

6. Determine the content for each meeting of the group:
   What is(are) the goal(s) for learning?
   How can main points be summarized?
   How can learning be interactive and still maintain focus?
   What skills can be practiced in the group?
   How much time can be allotted to discussion?
   What homework is to be done between this session and next?

7. Plan how to end the group well or how to help members join and leave an open-ended group:
   How will successful completion be determined?
   How will comments, kudos, and criticisms be obtained from participants?
   Will there be any post-participation follow-up or booster sessions?

lems and develop skills they will use in the future, requires some direction and specificity. For this reason, psychoeducational groups should emphasize learning and skill acquisition, in addition to social support. They should be sufficiently structured to maintain focus on the goals of the group, but flexible enough to accommodate individual differences among the group members.

Groups are not only a cost-effective means of delivering an intervention; they also provide opportunities for patients that are not available within the context of individual therapy. Groups particularly enhance such interventions as problem-solving, normalizing, social skills practice, and perhaps most importantly, the discovery that one is not alone with a frightening illness.

4.1.3   Pharmacotherapy

There have been very few randomized, controlled clinical trials of antidepressants for patients with coronary heart disease. A review of this literature found that only 12 such trials were published between 1966 and 1998, along with a small number of open label studies that examined the safety and side effects of various antidepressants for patients with CHD. A few additional clinical trials have been completed since this review was published. However, the number of studies is still quite small, and there are more questions than answers regarding the safety and efficacy of most of the available antidepressants for treating cardiac patients.

Most antidepressants belong to one of the following classes: tricyclic antidepressants (TCAs) such as imipramine and nortriptyline, monoamine oxidase inhibitors (MAOIs) such as phenelzine and isocarboxazid, second-generation antidepressants such as trazodone and buproprion, and selective serotonin reuptake inhibitors (SSRIs) such as fluoxetine and sertraline. Other psychiatric treatments for severe depression include electroconvulsive therapy (ECT) and newer, less well studied techniques such as transcranial magnetic stimulation (TMS) and vagal nerve stimulation (VNS). TMS and VNS have not yet been evaluated in cardiac patients, and they will not be considered here.

Clinical trials of TCAs for cardiac patients have generally found them to be efficacious. However, safety studies have found that both the TCAs and the MAOIs are contraindicated for many cardiac patients. These agents affect cardiac conduction and contractility, increase heart rate and blood pressure, trigger certain electrocardiographic abnormalities, and cause orthostatic hypotension in vulnerable patients. In most cases, these drugs should not be prescribed for cardiac patients with left bundle branch block, unstable angina, or congestive heart failure.

Some of the older antidepressants have cardiotoxic side effects and are seldom prescribed for patients with heart disease

Orthostatic hypotension, although not as much of a problem for younger patients, is a common complaint among older patients using these medications. This is of particular concern because older patients may become unstable and fall during hypotensive episodes. Hip fractures can be life-threatening injuries in elderly patients. Survivors require long recovery periods and tend to have a poor health-related quality of life.

Additional concerns about TCAs came to light following the Cardiac Arrhythmia Suppression Trial (CAST) of antiarrythmic therapy for post-MI patients. The CAST study found that type IA and IC antiarrhythmics actually *increase* the risk of cardiac mortality in these patients. TCAs obviously have antidepressant effects, but they are also classified as type IA antiarrhythmics. As a result of the CAST findings, many experts advise against using any of the older antidepressants in treating patients with coronary heart disease. Nevertheless, some cardiac patients can tolerate these agents and they are still prescribed in some cases.

Even fewer studies have evaluated the safety or the efficacy of the second generation antidepressants for cardiac patients. At high doses, bupropion, a weak inhibitor of norepinephrine and dopamine reuptake, tends to increase both blood pressure and heart rate. Trazodone, a weak blocker of serotonin reuptake, seems to have few cardiovascular side effects, but it has not been well studied in cardiac patients. There is at least some evidence that trazodone may increase the rate of premature ventricular contractions. However, none of the second generation antidepressants have received adequate study in patients with CHD.

Antidepressants belonging to the newest class, the selective serotonin reuptake inhibitors (SSRIs), seem to be relatively free of cardiac side effects. Unfortunately, as with the earlier drugs, there have been very few studies of these agents in patients with heart disease. However, there has been one relatively large study of the safety and efficacy of an SSRI, sertraline, for the treatment of depression in patients following an acute cardiac event. The Sertraline Antidepressant Heart Attack Randomized Trial (SADHART) evaluated the safety and efficacy of sertaline in depressed patients with a recent myocardial infarction or episode of unstable angina. SADHART was the first study to show that a specific antidepressant is safe for use early after an acute cardiac event. On the other hand, it showed that sertraline was only modestly effective in treating major depression. There was no overall difference in Hamilton Rating Scale for Depression scores between the sertraline and placebo groups. There was, however, a significant difference in Hamilton scores among patients with severe, recurrent major depressive disorder.

Sertraline has been proven in a large multicenter trial to be relatively safe for depressed post-MI patients

Despite their apparent safety in patients with coronary heart disease, there is evidence that the drug-drug interactions are potentially problematic for these patients. This is of concern because most patients have to take multiple medications for their heart disease, as well as for any other chronic, comorbid medical illnesses they may have, such as diabetes and hypertension. However, several different SSRIs are available, and not all interact with the same medications. Furthermore, many drug-drug interactions are predictable, so that physicians and pharmacists are usually able to avoid prescribing an SSRI that would interact with one or more of the patient's other medications. Alternative SSRIs can be considered when there is concern about a potentially harmful drug interaction. If a potential drug-drug interaction cannot be precluded altogether, side effects and blood levels of the drugs should be carefully monitored during treatment. Many experts believe that the SSRIs are reasonably safe when administered with appropriate precautions to patients with heart disease. Given their relative safety, SSRIs are being used with increasing frequency to treat depression in patients with CHD.

Neither the safety nor the efficacy of ECT has been adequately studied in patients with cardiovascular disease. Trials of ECT in elderly patients have generally found it to be safe and effective, but it has been recommended pri-

Nonadherence to prescribed antidepressants is common; behavioral interventions and case management can help to improve adherence

marily for patients who are refractory to antidepressants, or whose depression is both chronic and severe. Furthermore, the patient's blood pressure increases during and after ECT, and there have been reports of ischemic and arrhythmic complications in patients with heart disease. Thus, care must be exercised when treating depression with ECT in cardiac patients, and it is usually not recommended unless and until the patient has failed to respond to an adequate trial of antidepressant medications.

In summary, there have been few trials of pharmacological treatments for depression in patients with stable CHD, and only one randomized, controlled, multi-center clinical trial in patients with a recent acute cardiac event. More clinical trials are needed, but there is at least some evidence that depression in cardiac patients can be treated safely and effectively with carefully selected antidepressants.

4.1.4   Working with Families and Significant Others

Like most chronic illnesses, heart disease tends to affect all of the individuals who are actively involved in a patient's life. Because of the wealth of information about heart disease that is available, as well as information about its causes and treatments, it is rare to find family members who are completely without any knowledge of what they are facing. However, this can be a double-edged sword, as the predictions and expectations of family members may be based on misunderstood or incomplete information.

Heart disease occurs in the context of everything else that is going on in the lives of the patient and significant others, including births, deaths, child-rearing, divorces, work, and other medical problems. These other issues may be much more pressing than the heart disease itself for some patients. In some cases, the emergence of heart disease overwhelms an already-stressed family, and they find themselves unable to cope with the piling on of yet another problem.

The patient may not be the only member of his or her family with a serious medical illness

Consider, for instance, a heart patient who is suddenly unable to care for a chronically ill spouse, or a spouse who was about to begin divorce proceedings against the patient and who now feels trapped by the patient's need for care and the additional burden of guilt. When working with families who are facing numerous financial, social, and medical problems, take the time to understand how they have managed in the past and avoid prescribing routine solutions which they may have already found do not meet their particular needs. Such families often have considerable "survival experience." It is helpful to acknowledge and build upon the family's experience in coping with adversity.

Some of the best predictors of a family's ability to cope are their history of coping with other challenges, their overall stability, and their ability to communicate or tolerate limited communication. In each case, it is best if significant others support the goals of therapy and the therapeutic process. A seriously ill patient's participation in therapy may depend on a family member's willingness to help, for example, with transportation or with making sure that the patient is up, fed, and dressed in preparation for a treatment session. Meeting with the patient's spouse, partner, parents, or children to answer questions and obtain their viewpoints can be very helpful in eliciting their cooperation.

When a significant other is non-supportive or even overtly hostile, maintaining a positive attitude toward the family member can be helpful. This avoids placing the patient in the position of defending either party, and it supports stability in their relationship. When eliciting the views of a spouse or other family member, it sometimes becomes obvious that he or she may be having a harder time coping with the heart disease than the patient is. It may also become obvious that the patient is misrepresenting how well he or she is functioning in daily life. At this point, there are decisions to be made: whether to make therapy a family process, refer the spouse or other family member for separate therapy, work through the patient's own thoughts and behaviors to improve relationships, or obtain the patient's permission to have a session with another family member alone. How to proceed depends on many factors, but the guiding ethical principle should always be the welfare of the patient and respect for individual privacy and confidentiality.

When working with family members, several strategies are particularly useful. Begin with an assessment of the family's understanding of the patient's heart condition, of psychotherapy, and of their role in the process. Dispelling erroneous ideas about these issues is particularly important, but it must be done in a gentle and understanding manner. For example, "Mrs. Jones, I can well understand your concerns. If I thought for one minute that a therapist and my husband were going to sit around and blame me for everything, I wouldn't want anything to do with it either." Be sure to communicate respect for their knowledge, understanding, and insights into the person who was their parent, sibling, partner, or spouse long before becoming a patient of yours. If the patient has said *anything* positive about the family member it is helpful to communicate that fact, and doing so in general terms does not violate confidentiality. Make it clear that you consider all present to be allied in the cause of helping the patient; this, in turn, helps the family to cope with the patient's illness and to function better.

4.1.5   Working with Physicians and Other Health Care Providers

Physicians may be completely uninvolved in a patient's psychotherapy, or they may be involved in numerous ways from making the referral for therapy, to providing useful information, to discussing pharmacological treatments for psychiatric problems, to supporting continuation of therapy when a patient wants to terminate treatment prematurely. Although such a level of positive support is not common, neither is outright hostility to the therapeutic process. More cardiologists and their patients are becoming aware of at least some of the research on depression, anxiety, hostility and heart disease. It is your job to share your expertise and to educate physicians about current evidence in support of psychological interventions. It is also your job to eschew techniques and procedures for which there is no support in research or even reasonable theory.

Therapists who believe that they are not being given their due professional respect in a medical setting may react with anger, resentment, or reticence to express their opinions or offer insights about their patients. Some of this is due to the centuries-long head start that physicians have in the medical environment and to the fact that this environment is to a large extent theirs, but it is also due to the fact that psychotherapists often speak a different language than physicians and fail to communicate the proven value of what they have to offer to medical patients.

When interacting with medical staff, nurses, patient care technicians, physical therapists, and other health care professionals, communicate your respect for what they know and do, as well as respect for what *you* know and have to offer. In order to make their environment your environment, remember these points:

Table 15
Working with Medical Staff

- Become knowledgeable of medical terms and use them as appropriate
- Become knowledgeable about basic cardiac physiology; know what's expected and what's unusual during recovery
- Become knowledgeable of a few basic cardiology tests and results
- Become knowledgeable about your patients' other medical problems
- Learn to present information concisely
- Avoid using psychological jargon
- Offer suggestions that are helpful, practical, realistic, and evidence-based
- Keep up with current research supporting your recommendations
- Recognize that issues you consider to be of utmost importance may not coincide with the concerns of others involved your patients' care
- When in the hospital, know that everyone there has more to do than time allows
- Be understanding of staff frustration with challenging patients
- Seek the advice and expertise of other staff members
- Always speak of the patient and their problems respectfully and professionally
- Within the limits of confidentiality, keep physicians informed of their patients' progress and call when suspected medical problems are encountered
- Refer patients to physicians and other specialists as appropriate

As you gain experience in working with cardiac patients, you will develop a store of knowledge and experience that is unique to your specialty and is shared by no one else on the medical care team. But just as it is important to respect and share your expertise, it is important to remain interested in learning even more. When possible, attend medical presentations and meetings that can provide you with updates on treatments and medications which may be offered to your patients. These events also provide an opportunity get to know physicians who care for your patients and for them to meet you. If the opportunity arises for you to present a workshop or give a presentation to a support group, prepare well and present yourself as a colleague with the ability to make significant contributions to the welfare of patients. If what you have to offer reliably eases the burden of busy physicians, this too can improve trust and increase referrals. In the end, physicians are often guided by positive reports from their patients or their office staff, so be sure to make an effort to establish good relationships with everyone you encounter in your professional life.

4.2   Mechanisms of Action

All of the empirically-supported treatments for depression and anxiety discussed in this chapter were assumed by their developers to exert their therapeutic effects through particular mechanisms of action. However, the *actual* mechanisms of action often differ from the hypothesized ones. A number of studies have challenged conventional assumptions about how these treatments work.

The single most important mechanism in all of these interventions is the **placebo effect**. A number of influential meta-analyses and other systematic reviews have concluded that currently available antidepressant medications are significantly more efficacious than pill placebos, but by a disappointingly small margin. More of the therapeutic benefit of current antidepressants is attributable to their placebo value than to their specific antidepressant effects on neurotransmitter systems in the brain. A recent review considered whether this might be due to an unintended source of bias in clinical trials: inert placebos have no physiological side effects, but antidepressants do. It is possible that these side effects lead to worse depression outcomes for patients who are randomly assigned to receive the actual drugs. To address this question, the review examined only studies that utilized **active placebos**, i.e., pills that do not contain an active antidepressant agent but that do cause similar side effects.

In clinical trials, the severity of depression often improves about 50% in the antidepressant group and about 30% in the placebo group

The review found that the effects of antidepressant medications are significantly larger than the effects of active placebo, but the differences were still fairly small. The most important implication for clinicians is that we need more effective antidepressants than the ones that are currently on the market. Many patients benefit from the current generation of antidepressants, but not all of them do. This is all the more urgent for clinicians who treat depression in cardiac patients, since few antidepressants have been shown to be safe for patients with heart disease. For example, SADHART demonstrated that sertraline is safe for patients recovering from an acute MI, but many cardiac patients who can tolerate sertraline do not respond to it. This leaves clinicians wondering which antidepressant to try if sertraline fails. Of course, they should also consider the psychotherapeutic options!

There have also been persistent questions about the role of placebo effects and other nonspecific factors in psychotherapy. Although they undoubtedly play important roles in IPT and CBT, the current weight of evidence indicates that both of the interventions are more efficacious than pill placebos and other nonspecific control conditions. This was not evident in the TDCRP, but it has been observed in other studies. One recent study, for example, compared the short-term effects of CBT to those of a supportive-counseling-placebo intervention for outpatients with major depression. CBT had both statistically and clinically significant advantages over the control intervention.

Since the placebo effect is such an important ingredient, clinicians should try to make the best use of it. This is especially important for depressed patients, since feeling hopeless and discouraged is an integral part of depression. By conveying their optimism about the benefits of treatment and the prospects for improvement, clinicians can overturn their patients' pessimistic expectations and improve their ability to achieve remission.

The evidence for modality-specific effects in the treatment of depression is sparse at best

The placebo effect may account for a substantial proportion of the effects of these treatments, but what accounts for the benefits that they produce above and beyond their placebo value? This differs from one treatment to the next, and much remains to be learned about these mechanisms. However, this is an active area of research. For example, Dr. Michael Thase and his colleagues collected electroencephalographic (EEG) sleep data on a group of patients with major depression before and after 16 weeks of CBT. They found that certain EEG sleep abnormalities predicted worse depression outcomes. They subsequently reported that in most cases, some of these sleep disturbances improved as the patient's depression improved over the course of treatment. A minority of patients continued to have sleep disturbances even after their depression remitted, and these patients were found to be at high risk of relapse. EEG sleep abnormalities are not explicitly targeted in CBT for depression, yet they seem to play an important role in the process of recovery. This underscores the fact that we need to learn much more about the specific mechanisms that are responsible for therapeutic gains.

4.3   Efficacy and Prognosis

Cardiac patients have been systematically excluded from most antidepressant clinical trials

There have been relatively few randomized, controlled clinical trials of treatments for comorbid depressive or anxiety disorders in cardiac patients, or in any other population of medically ill patients for that matter. Much of what is known about efficacy and prognosis is based on studies that have actually *excluded* medically ill patients. To our knowledge, there have not been any controlled clinical trials of treatments for depression or anxiety in which the participants have been stratified according to whether they have heart disease. This type of study could tell us, for example, whether CBT and IPT are as effective for depression in patients with heart disease as they are for medically well patients. Despite the lack of such studies, practice must be based on the best available evidence, both from studies of medically well subjects and of medically ill patients.

4.4   Combination Therapy

It is difficult to conduct clinical trials comparing monotherapies to combination therapies with adequate statistical power, and the evidence regarding this question is inconsistent. Nevertheless, a number of studies have suggested that short-term depression outcomes tend to be somewhat better, and relapse rates somewhat lower, among patients with major depression who receive a combination of CBT and antidepressants than among those who receive monotherapy. Some studies have also suggested that certain combination therapies may be helpful for patients with anxiety disorders. For example, Dr. David Barlow and his colleagues recently reported a study in which patients with panic disorder were randomly assigned to CBT only, placebo only, CBT plus imipramine, or CBT plus placebo. Both of the active treatments produced significantly better short-term outcomes than the placebo-only condition, but the combination therapy was no more efficacious than either monotherapy. During the maintenance phase, however, patients who had received combination therapy tended to have lower relapse rates than patients who had received CBT alone or CBT plus placebo.

CBT plus imipramine may be a useful combination in panic disorder

4.5　　Problems in Carrying Out Treatment

Heart disease and other medical illnesses pose a number of barriers to the delivery of treatments for depression and other psychosocial problems. For example, most patients with heart disease are already taking several medications by the time they are referred for psychiatric or psychological care. Many are reluctant to add yet another medication to their regimen, and many others are unable to afford the expense even if they are willing to take the drug. In some cases, the patient's regimen can be simplified to make it easier to accommodate psychopharmacological treatments.

Medical illness can also make it difficult for patients to participate in psychotherapeutic interventions. For example, many patients with congestive heart failure are too ill or debilitated to make an extra trip to a clinic once a week for psychotherapy sessions, even if they would very much like to receive treatment. Recent studies have attempted to address this problem by conducting psychotherapy sessions by telephone. There have been very few direct comparisons of the efficacy of in-person vs telephone-based therapy. However, a growing number of studies have demonstrated that CBT can be delivered efficaciously via telephone. For example, researchers at the Group Health Cooperative in Seattle recently conducted a large, randomized clinical trial in which they compared usual primary care for depression to telephone care management, and to telephone care management plus telephone CBT for depressed primary care patients who were starting antidepressant treatment. Participation rates were extremely high: 97% in the telephone care management group and 93% in the group receiving both care management and CBT via telephone. The telephone psychotherapy group had significantly better outcomes than the usual care group, and better outcomes than the care management group. This is some of the best evidence to date that CBT can be delivered efficaciously via telephone to patients who would otherwise not be amenable to intervention. It is an especially promising development for patients with heart disease, particularly those with debilitating conditions such as advanced congestive heart failure.

Telephone-based CBT has been used successfully to treat patients for whom frequent clinic visits would be impractical

5

Case Vignettes

Case 1: A Woman in her Sixties with Heart Disease and Diabetes

According to her son, Mrs. G had spent very little time out of bed since her cardiac bypass surgery six months earlier. Prior to her surgery, she had remained active after retiring from a physically demanding job in a nursing home. When she was asked to consider participating in a clinical trial of treatment for depression after heart surgery, she reluctantly agreed at her son's urging. He reported to the study interviewer, "I'm watching my mother die before my eyes." Because she lacked transportation from her semi-rural home to the clinic, Mrs. G was seen at home for the entire 12-week protocol.

At the initial visit, Mrs. G asked the therapist to enter the home without getting up from the couch. She looked pale and exhausted, and she spoke in short sentences with a whispery voice. She reported that she was spending most of her nights on the couch watching television and much of the day in bed. She worried constantly about her health, believed that she would not live long, and had lost interest in most activities, including talking with family members on the phone. She said that she felt quite sad, cried off and on, and did not expect to ever feel any better.

Therapy began with eliciting her fears and normalizing her reactions. It soon became clear that she had a poor understanding of her heart surgery and of what to expect during her recovery. In order to address some of her anxious thoughts about her situation and her future, Mrs. G was given an opportunity to ask questions about her heart disease, what was done in her surgery, and what her physicians had reported about her hospital course. Although many therapists shy away from discussing medical information with patients, once a therapist develops some expertise in a particular area, discussing basic facts can be very helpful so long as medical interpretation is avoided. It is likely that Mrs. G had already been told much of what was discussed in therapy, but like most patients, she had retained very little of the information she received in the days following surgery.

Mrs. G was very short of breath and experienced mild chest pain with any exertion. She had interpreted this to mean that activity was dangerous for her. As weeks turned to months, she became progressively weaker and deconditioned. She had attempted cardiac rehabilitation at her physician's insistence but this was terminated because of unrelated health problems. Mrs. G's symptoms and what her physician had told her were discussed at length. Her records indicated that an internal mammary artery was used for bypass. Because of the dislocation of nerves and decreased blood flow to chest wall muscles, patients often continue to have tingling, pin-prick pain, and numbness for a long time after surgery, which is precisely the sensation she described. Using drawings, the source of her discomfort was explained to her satisfaction. Then her shortness of breath was discussed. The fact that virtually every post-bypass patient feels weak and short of breath for a while after surgery was explained. The role of inactivity in maintaining or even worsening her symptoms was also explained. Her likely ability to reverse this process was discussed, and she reported feeling hopeful for the first time in months. As a therapeutic homework assignment, Mrs. G was asked to get up and walk around her small home once or twice every hour between TV shows. A simple graph was created on notebook paper for her to record her walks and any reactions she noticed.

At the next few sessions, Mrs. G talked further about her fears and about the activities she missed. Weekly homework consisted of increases in walking, working toward solving some problems with obtaining medications, and securing transportation. As her walking progressed, her symptoms subsided. At the 6th session, she answered the door and she began taking walks outside and talking with neighbors. One of her neighbors offered to drive her to a different church and she accepted. She also found out about a senior center in town and the availability of bus transportation that could pick her up at her door. By the end of therapy, she was going to the senior center daily for lunch and even went on a weekend outing with other church members. Her depression and anxiety had resolved. Problems with some of her relatives remained unresolved, but she had decided to accept the ongoing discord as part of life and focus more on her new friends.

This case illustrates how frightening heart disease and surgery can be, especially when information is either not given clearly or is misunderstood. The cornerstone of her treatment was behavioral activation, but this could not occur until her fears and misconceptions were addressed. Once physically able, Mrs. G was ready to seek social support and more fulfilling activities than watching television. Another important aspect of this intervention was making it clear, both implicitly and explicitly, that Mrs. G's improvement was due to her own efforts. Although she continued to have health problems, she also continued her active lifestyle and positive attitude because she became aware of her own ability to solve problems and prevail over limitations.

Patients such as Mrs. G, with limited education, are often not given the detailed information they need to understand their physician's recommendations, and they are unsure of what questions to ask. An experienced therapist familiar with heart disease can make educated guesses about questions patients might have and bring them up as typical concerns. This normalizes their lack of knowledge and encourages more questioning and verbalization of concerns, thereby making it possible to address psychological barriers to rehabilitation.

Case 2: A Man in his Fifties with Congestive Heart Failure

Mr. C came into therapy of his own accord, having had cognitive behavior therapy about six years earlier after an MI. Both the prior and current therapies were conducted under research protocols In the intervening years, he had done well despite many challenges, but now found it difficult to cope with worsening CHF and premature retirement from work that he had enjoyed. Due to severe heart failure with a low ejection fraction, he was very short of breath, had limited energy, and required daily naps to combat his fatigue. Despite this, he drove himself to therapy for most of his sessions. It was important to make sure that a room with a comfortable temperature was available because, like most CHF patients, he had very poor tolerance for heat and cold.

Mr. C reported that he had been feeling quite depressed for the past few months and at times had felt suicidal. He believed that he was contributing little to his family and had become a burden. He described himself as worthless. He denied any plan to commit suicide and insisted he would never take his life because of the effects it would have on his family and because of his belief that suicide was cowardly. However, he clearly had the means to end his life simply by not taking his medications. This is a fact of life for most patients with CHF, and they are well aware of it.

The first part of therapy centered on addressing his beliefs about his worth and developing a sense of hope about what he still might be able to do in his life. For this, straightforward cognitive techniques were used to help him analyze his most distressing thoughts and refute them with facts. Mr. C considered his role as breadwinner to be his most important contribution, but his family had clearly indicated that they believed otherwise. In fact, they had long wished that he had spent more time at home. One of his homework assignments was making a list of all that he was in addition to being a breadwinner. To his surprise, this list was extensive, as was the list of his current contributions to the welfare of his family. The list of what his family actually had to do for him on a regular basis was quite short.

It was not long before Mr. C was ready to address core beliefs. As a young man, he had worked for his father, who had been a stern taskmaster and extremely difficult to please. Mr. C discovered that he developed his sense of worth based primarily on what his father had taught him about being a man. He had come to believe that a man's worth was based on hard work – being reliable, making a good living, providing the "extras" for his family and doing everything to perfection. Men who took vacations were considered lazy. This belief was unshakeable until other beliefs held by Mr. C's father were also explored, including beliefs that Mr. C. clearly rejected. In time, Mr. C realized that his father was simply wrong some of the time, much like the rest of us. It was not hard, in this context, for Mr. C to begin to question his harsh judgments about his own worth.

For the next phase of therapy, problem-solving was employed. The **activity-rest cycle**, also called **time-based pacing,** had been introduced early in therapy to enable him to be more active. This technique is used to combat the belief that one has to keep at a job until it is completed even if dangerously fatigued, because this leads to a need for prolonged rest, which is also counterproductive. Instead, the patient is taught to self-monitor in order to discover the length of time he can work comfortably. He should stop at this point, whether a chore is completed or not, and rest for a fixed period of time. Then the chore can be resumed without severe fatigue. In this way, patients accomplish their goals while retaining some reserve energy.

Mr. C had been asked to do some consulting work which he desperately wanted to do, but found the very thought of it overwhelming and dysphoria-inducing. He was encouraged to utilize a problem-solving approach to the possibility of doing some part-time work. He determined that he could break the work down into manageable steps with planned days of rest in between. He presented his plan to the prospective employer who agreed to have the work done on the schedule Mr. C had proposed. Mr. C had the foresight to build room in the schedule for exacerbations of his illness. Because of this, he was able to continue working, albeit on a limited basis, in an occupation that offered him fulfillment and a small income.

Two more beliefs were particularly challenging for Mr. C: that he could not enjoy activities until he felt much better, and that socializing with others always meant that they would be focused on his limitations and that they would react with either impatience or pity. He spent time on his own examining his thoughts and testing them for accuracy. Then he conducted some behavioral experiments and discovered that his distressing predictions had been wrong. He further learned that he could react differently than he had in the past if others did react poorly to his physical slowness. After changing his attitude about living with his illness, Mr. C went on some enjoyable family outings, including restful weekends away with his wife, and attended some meetings with others in his type of business.

Mr. C was visited in the hospital the day before he died suddenly of a heart attack. He reported that he was in a good mood, was spending some time working on a project, and was hopeful that that he would get back to his previous level of activity within a few days. Throughout his long illness and many setbacks, Mr. C found ways to remain involved in his work, his family, and his spiritual life, and was thus an inspiration and source of joy to those who knew him.

Case 3: A Man in his Seventies who Had Had a Heart Attack, Open Heart Surgery, and a Stroke

Mr. L came into therapy after a research protocol was offered and the therapist agreed to see him at his home. He reported feeling sad, angry, and disappointed with the outcome of his operation and with himself for continuing smoking. One of his oft-repeated phrases was, "Life's a bitch and then you die." He intended to use therapy to quit smoking and had some hope of returning to the golf course. Despite being financially secure, he worried much of the time about decreases in his investments and about his wife doing the chores he believed that he should be doing. He exhibited great pride in all that he had accomplished in a life of hard work building a business and in the improvements he had made to their house and yard. His sense of humor had remained intact, but tended toward the sardonic.

A substantial proportion of the time in Mr. L's therapy was devoted to helping him to become aware of his negative thinking patterns and to analyze them for errors. He did homework the first couple of weeks of therapy and thereafter reported forgetting to do it or not feeling like it. When discussing various difficulties in his life, he responded with blaming most of his problems on his failure to quit smoking and on being nagged about it. With some misgivings, his therapist relented and made smoking cessation a more central component of his therapy. While in treatment, he also tried a couple of alternative therapies in hope of overcoming his desire to smoke. After a discussion with his physician, nicotine patches and bupropion were tried but he did not tolerate them.

Another aim of therapy was behavioral activation. The goals were to improve his mood and to increase his engagement in activities that were inconsistent with smoking. To this end, one therapy session was held at the local driving range. He enjoyed seeing some of his friends but had a very hard time with the fact that his strength and accuracy had decreased considerably. He reacted more positively to tutoring his therapist in the finer points of holding and swinging a golf club.

In addition to smoking cessation and behavioral activation, Mr. L was given behavioral and cognitive assignments designed to help him become more aware of the abilities he retained, the positive aspects of his life, and the possibilities for continued improvement. In the end, standard smoking cessation techniques resulted in a day or two of abstinence followed by relapse. He also continued to have several alcoholic drinks when out for dinner, which was a frequent activity. His behavioral activation assignments were a little more successful, and he began spending more time walking to increase his stamina.

At the end of twelve weeks, Mr. L showed some improvement but his depression had not fully remitted. About seven months later, he called to report that he had finally made up his mind to quit smoking and said, "I feel so good I hardly know what to do with myself." He also said that he really didn't know how he came to achieve success. It appeared to him to have "just happened." Several months after that, he called to say that he had resumed smoking, was disgusted with himself, and felt very depressed. He refused a referral for therapy stating that he did not believe that he could get used to someone new.

Whether Mr. L would have had a more positive outcome with longer term therapy or with different interventions is unknown. It is possible that his stroke may have had something to do with Mr. L's rigid thinking style and concrete approach to novel ideas. However, the physical signs of his stroke were short-lived, and testing to determine the precise location of cerebral damage was not undertaken. In years past, outside the context of a research protocol, Mr. L would have remained in therapy longer in order to achieve full remission. In recent times, three months or more of weekly psychotherapy for depression is rarely approved for insurance coverage. However, patients like Mr. L can take quite a while to settle in to therapy and become comfortable with questioning their longstanding beliefs, attitudes, and habits.

Several strategies were suggested when Mr. L's case was reviewed at a clinical staff meeting, including: 1) to stay with the issue of his self-blaming thoughts until he successfully refutes them, 2) to work with his physician and/or a psychiatrist to come up with a tolerable antidepressant regimen, and 3) to work with his family to set up ongoing environmental reinforcements. At his last follow-up contact, Mr. L reported having good days and bad days, and continuing to be active with his hobbies and social outings.

6

Further Reading

This section included key references to literature where the practitioner can find further details or background information. Each reference includes a brief (2–5 lines) annotation.

Beck, J.S. (1995). *Cognitive therapy: Basics and beyond.* New York: Guilford Press. This excellent text provides clear information about the core principles and techniques of cognitive therapy as well as sound advice for working with challenging patients.

Levenson, J.L. (Ed.). (2005). *Textbook of psychosomatic medicine.* Washington, DC: American Psychiatric Publishing.
A textbook found in medical school libraries, written for psychiatrists. Probably the most up-to-date and comprehensive text on the current understanding of and treatment for psychological aspects of medical problems.

DiTomasso, R.A., Martin, D.M., & Kovnat, K.D. (2000). Medical patients in crisis. In F.M. Datillo & A. Freeman (Eds.), *Cognitive-behavioral strategies in crisis intervention* (pp. 409–428). New York: Guilford Press.
Brief, straightforward rationale and treatment instruction.

Sheps, D.H., & Rozanski, A. (Eds.) Depression and heart disease: Epidemiology, pathophysiology, & treatment [Special Issue]. *Psychosomatic Medicine, 67*(Suppl.1).

Taylor, G.J. (2005). *Primary care cardiology* (2nd ed.). Malden, MA: Blackwell.
A concise, clinically-relevant text written with great clarity. Readers with little or no background in pathophysiology may find it challenging at first, but it is worth the effort.

7

References

Alvarez, W., Jr., & Pickworth, K.K. (2003). Safety of antidepressant drugs in the patient with cardiac disease: A review of the literature. *Pharmacotherapy, 23,* 754–771.

Barlow DH, Gorman JM, Shear MK, Woods SW. (2000). Cognitive-behavioral therapy, imipramine, or their combination for panic disorder: A randomized controlled trial. *Journal of the American Medical Association, 283,* 2529–2536.

Beck, A.T., Rush, A.J., Shaw, B.E., & Emery, G. (1979). *Cognitive therapy of depression.* New York: Guilford Press.

Beck, J.S. (1995). *Cognitive therapy: Basics and beyond.* New York: Guilford Press.

Beck, J.S. (2005). *Cognitive therapy for challenging problems: What to do when the basics don't work.* New York: Guilford Press.

Berkman, L.F., Blumenthal, J., Burg, M., Carney, R.M., Catellier, D., Cowan, M.J. et al. (2003). Effects of treating depression and low perceived social support on clinical events after myocardial infarction: The Enhancing Recovery in Coronary Heart Disease Patients (ENRICHD) Randomized Trial. *Journal of the American Medical Association, 289,* 3106–3116.

Berkman LF, Leo-Summers L, Horwitz RI. (1992). Emotional support and survival after myocardial infarction. A prospective, population-based study of the elderly. *Annals of Internal Medicine, 117,* 1003–1009.

Berkman LF, Syme SL. (1979). Social networks, host resistance, and mortality: A nine-year follow-up study of Alameda County residents. *American Journal of Epidemiology, 109,* 186–204.

Blumenthal JA, Sherwood A, Babyak MA, Watkins LL, Waugh R, Georgiades A, Bacon SL, Hayano J, Coleman RE, Hinderliter A. (2005). Effects of exercise and stress management training on markers of cardiovascular risk in patients with ischemic heart disease: A randomized controlled trial. *Journal of the American Medical Association, 293,* 1626–1634.

Braunwald, E. (2001). *Essential atlas of heart diseases* (2nd ed.). Philadelphia: Developed by Current Medicine.

Brotman, A.W. (1985). Cardiac effects of ECT. *Biological Therapies in Psychiatry, 8,* 33.

Brummett BH, Barefoot JC, Siegler IC, Clapp-Channing NE, Lytle BL, Bosworth HB, Williams RB Jr, Mark DB. (2001). Characteristics of socially isolated patients with coronary artery disease who are at elevated risk for mortality. *Psychosomatic Medicine, 63,* 267–272.

Carney, R.M., Blumenthal, J.A., Stein, P.K., Watkins, L., Catellier, D., Berkman, L.F. et al. (2001). Depression, heart rate variability, and acute myocardial infarction. *Circulation, 104,* 2024–2028.

Carney, R.M., Freedland, K.E., & Sheps, D.S. (2004). Depression is a risk factor for mortality in coronary heart disease. *Psychosomatic Medicine, 66,* 799–801.

Carney, R.M., Blumenthal, J.A., Freedland, K.E., Youngblood, M., Veith, R.C., Burg, M.M. et al. (2004). Depression and late mortality after myocardial infarction in the Enhancing Recovery in Coronary Heart Disease (ENRICHD) study. *Psychosomatic Medicine, 66,* 466–474.

Carney, R.M., Freedland, K.E., & Sheps, D.S. (2004). Depression is a risk factor for mortality in coronary heart disease. *Psychosomatic Medicine, 66,* 799–801.

Carney, R.M., Freedland, K.E., Jaffe, A.S., Frasure-Smith, N., Lespérance, F., Sheps, D.S. et al. (2004). Depression as a risk factor for post-MI mortality. *Journal of the American College of Cardiology, 44,* 472–474.

Case RB, Moss AJ, Case N, McDermott M, Eberly S. (1992). Living alone after myocardial infarction. Impact on prognosis. *Journal of the American Medical Association, 267,* 515–519.

Caspi, A., Sugden, K., Moffitt, T.E., Taylor, A., Craig, I.W., Harrington, H. et al. (2003). Influence of life stress on depression: Moderation by a polymorphism in the 5-HTT gene. *Science, 301,* 386–389.

CAST Investigators (1989). Preliminary report: Effect of encainide and flecainide on mortality in a randomized trial of arrhythmia suppression after myocardial infarction. The Cardiac Arrhythmia Suppression Trial (CAST) Investigators. *New England Journal of Medicine, 321,* 406–412.

Cooper, R., Cutler, J., Svigne-Nickens, P., Fortmann, S.P., Friedman, L., Havlik, R. et al. (2000). Trends and disparities in coronary heart disease, stroke, and other cardiovascular diseases in the United States: Findings of the national conference on cardiovascular disease prevention. *Circulation, 102,* 3137–3147.

Cowan MJ, Pike KC, Budzynski HK. (2001). Psychosocial nursing therapy following sudden cardiac arrest: Impact on two-year survival. *Nursing Research, 50,* 68–76.

Dattilio, F.M., & Freeman, A. (2000). *Cognitive-behavioral strategies in crisis intervention* (2nd ed.). New York: Guilford Press.

Davies, S.J., Jackson, P.R., Potokar, J., & Nutt, D.J. (2004). Treatment of anxiety and depressive disorders in patients with cardiovascular disease. *British Medical Journal, 328,* 939–943.

Denollet J. (2005). DS14: standard assessment of negative affectivity, social inhibition, and Type D personality. *Psychosomatic Medicine, 67,* 89–97.

DeRubeis RJ, Hollon SD, Amsterdam JD, Shelton RC, Young PR, Salomon RM, O›Reardon JP, Lovett ML, Gladis MM, Brown LL, Gallop R. (2005). Cognitive therapy vs medications in the treatment of moderate to severe depression. *Archives of General Psychiatry, 62,* 409–416.

Elkin I, Shea MT, Watkins JT, Imber SD, Sotsky SM, Collins JF, Glass DR, Pilkonis PA, Leber WR, Docherty JP, et al. (1989). National Institute of Mental Health Treatment of Depression Collaborative Research Program. General effectiveness of treatments. *Archives of General Psychiatry, 46,* 971–982.

Fisher EB Jr. (1997). Two approaches to social support in smoking cessation: Commodity model and nondirective support. *Addictive Behavior, 22,* 819–833.

Frasure-Smith, N., Lespérance, F., Gravel, G., Masson, A., Juneau, M., Talajic, M. et al. (2000). Social support, depression, and mortality during the first year after myocardial infarction. *Circulation, 101,* 1919–1924.

Frasure-Smith, N., Lespérance, F., Gravel, G., Masson, A., Juneau, M., & Bourassa, M.G. (2002). Long-term survival differences among low-anxious, high-anxious and repressive copers enrolled in the Montreal Heart Attack Readjustment Trial. *Psychosomatic Medicine, 64,* 571–579.

Frasure-Smith, N., & Lespérance, F. (2003). Depression: A cardiac risk factor in search of a treatment. *Journal of the American Medical Association, 289,* 3171–3173.

Frasure-Smith, N. & Lespérance, F. (2003). Depression and other psychological risks following myocardial infarction. *Archives of General Psychiatry, 60,* 627–636.

Freedland, K.E., Rich, M.W., Skala, J.A., Carney, R.M., Vila-Roman, V.G., & Jaffe, A.S. (2003). Prevalence of depression in hospitalized patients with congestive heart failure. *Psychosomatic Medicine, 65,* 119–128.

Frizelle DJ, Lewin RJ, Kaye G, Hargreaves C, Hasney K, Beaumont N, Moniz-Cook E. (2004). Cognitive-behavioural rehabilitation programme for patients with an implanted ardioverter defibrillator: a pilot study. *British Journal of Health Psychology, 9,* 381–392.

Furze G, Bull P, Lewin RJ, Thompson DR. (2003). Development of the York Angina Beliefs Questionnaire. *Journal of Health Psychology, 8,* 307–315.

Gerring, J.P., & Shields, H.M. (1982). The identification and management of patients with a high risk for cardiac arrhythmias during modified ECT. *Journal of Clinical Psychiatry, 43,* 140–143.

Glassman, A.H., Roose, S.P., & Bigger, J.T., Jr. (1993). The safety of tricyclic antidepressants in cardiac patients. Risk-benefit reconsidered. *Journal of the American Medical Association, 269,* 2673–2675.

Glassman, A.H., O'Connor, C.M., Califf, R.M., Swedberg, K., Schwartz, P., Bigger, J.T., Jr. et al. (2002). Sertraline treatment of major depression in patients with acute MI or unstable angina. *Journal of the American Medical Association, 288,* 701–709.

Goldberg, A.D., Becker, L.C., Bonsall, R., Cohen, J.D., Ketterer, M.W., Kaufman, P.G. et al. (1996). Ischemic, hemodynamic, and neurohormonal responses to mental and exercise stress – Experience from the psychophysiological investigations of Myocardial Ischemia Study (PIMI). *Circulation, 94,* 2402–2409.

Haas, L.J. (2004). *Handbook of primary care psychology.* Oxford: Oxford University Press.

Harland, J., White, M., Drinkwater, C., Chinn, D., Farr, L., & Howel, D. (1999). The Newcastle exercise project: A randomised controlled trial of methods to promote physical activity in primary care. *British Medical Journal, 319,* 828–832.

Hollon SD, DeRubeis RJ, Shelton RC, Amsterdam JD, Salomon RM, O›Reardon JP, Lovett ML, Young PR, Haman KL, Freeman BB, Gallop R. (2005). Prevention of relapse following cognitive therapy vs medications in moderate to severe depression. *Archives of General Psychiatry, 62,* 417–422.

Kaufmann, P.G. (2003). Depression in cardiovascular disease: Can the risk be reduced? *Biological Psychiatry, 54,* 187–190.

Keller MB, McCullough JP, Klein DN, Arnow B, Dunner DL, Gelenberg AJ, Markowitz JC, Nemeroff CB, Russell JM, Thase ME, Trivedi MH, Zajecka J. (2000). A comparison of nefazodone, the cognitive behavioral-analysis system of sychotherapy, and their combination for the treatment of chronic depression. *New England Journal of Medicine, 342,* 1462–1470.

Kranitz, L., & Lehrer, P. (2004). Biofeedback applications in the treatment of cardiovascular diseases. *Cardiology in Review, 12,* 177–181.

Krantz, D.S., Sheps, D.S., Carney, R.M., & Natelson, B.H. (2000). Effects of mental stress in patients with coronary artery disease: Evidence and clinical implications. *JAMA, 283,* 1800–1802.

Levenson, J.L., & American, P.P. (2005). *The American Psychiatric Publishing textbook of psychosomatic medicine.* Washington, DC: American Psychiatric Publishing.

Lewin RJ, Furze G, Robinson J, Griffith K, Wiseman S, Pye M, Boyle R. (2002). A randomised controlled trial of a self-management plan for patients with newly diagnosed angina. *British Journal of General Practice, 52,* 194–196, 199–201.

Little, P., Dorward, M., Gralton, S., Hammerton, L., Pillinger, J., White, P. et al. (2004). A randomised controlled trial of three pragmatic approaches to initiate increased physical activity in sedentary patients with risk factors for cardiovascular disease. *British Journal of General Practice, 54,* 189–195.

Lovallo, W.R. (1997). *Stress and health: Biological and psychological interactions.* Thousand Oaks: Sage.

McCullough, J.P., Jr. (2003). Treatment for chronic depression using Cognitive Behavioral Analysis System of Psychotherapy (CBASP). *Journal of Clinical Psychology, 59,* 833–846.

Miller, W.R. (1993). What really drives change? *Addiction, 88,* 1479–1480.

Miller, W.R. (1996). Motivational interviewing: Research, practice, and puzzles. *Addictive Behaviors, 21,* 835–842.

Miller, W.R., & Rollnick, S. (2002). *Motivational interviewing: Preparing people for change* (2nd ed.). New York: Guilford Press.

Miller, W.R. (2005). Motivational interviewing and the incredible shrinking treatment effect. *Addiction, 100,* 421.

Murray, C.J., & Lopez, A.D. (1997). Global mortality, disability, and the contribution of risk factors: Global Burden of Disease Study. *Lancet, 349,* 1436–1442.

Murray, C.J. & Lopez, A.D. (1997). Mortality by cause for eight regions of the world: Global burden of disease study. *Lancet, 349,* 1269–1276.

Nezu, A.M. (1986). Efficacy of a social problem-solving therapy approach for unipolar depression. *Journal of Consulting and Clinical Psychology, 34,* 196–202.

Nezu, A.M., Nezu, C.M., Felgoise, S.H., McClure, K.S., & Houts, P.S. (2003). Project Genesis: Assessing the efficacy of problem-solving therapy for distressed adult cancer patients. *Journal of Consulting and Clinical Psychology, 71,* 1036–1048.

Pary, R., Tobias, C.R., & Lippmann, S. (1989). Antidepressants and the cardiac patient. Selecting an appropriate medication. *Postgraduate Medicine, 85,* 267–76.

Pollin, I.S., & Holland, J. (1992). A model for counseling the medically ill: The Linda Pollin Foundation approach. Introduction. *General Hospital Psychiatry, 14,* 1S–2S.

Pollin, I.S., & Kanaan, S.B. (1995). *Medical crisis counseling: Short-term therapy for long-term illness.* New York: Norton.

Roose, S.P., Katz, I.R., Pollock, B.G., & Valuck, R.J. (2002). Contemporary issues in the diagnosis and treatment of late-life depression. *Journal of the American Medical Directors Association, 3,* H26–H29.

Roose, S.P. (2003). Treatment of depression in patients with heart disease. *Biological Psychiatry, 54,* 262–268.

Rosengren, A., Hawken, S., Ounpuu, S., Sliwa, K., Zubaid, M., Almahmeed, W.A. et al. (2004). Association of psychosocial risk factors with risk of acute myocardial infarction in 11,119 cases and 13,648 controls from 52 countries (the INTERHEART study): Case-control study. *Lancet, 364,* 953–962.

Sheline, Y.I., Freedland, K.E., & Carney, R.M. (1997). How safe are serotonin reuptake inhibitors for depression in patients with coronary heart disease? *American Journal of Medicine, 102,* 54–59.

Shores, M.M., Pascualy, M., & Veith, R.C. (1998). Major depression and heart disease: Treatment trials. *Seminars in Clinical Neuropsychiatry, 3,* 87–101.

Smith, D.E., Heckemeyer, C.M., Kratt, P.P., & Mason, D.A. (1997). Motivational interviewing to improve adherence to a behavioral weight-control program for older obese women with NIDDM. A pilot study. *Diabetes Care, 20,* 52–54.

Taylor, G.J. (2005). *Primary care cardiology* (2nd ed.). Malden, MA: Blackwell.

Thase ME, Kupfer DJ, Fasiczka AJ, Buysse DJ, Simons AD, Frank E. (1997). Identifying an abnormal electroencephalographic sleep profile to characterize major depressive disorder. *Biological Psychiatry, 41,* 964–973.

Truelsen, T., Mahonen, M., Tolonen, H., Asplund, K., Bonita, R., & Vanuzzo, D. (2003). Trends in stroke and coronary heart disease in the WHO MONICA Project. *Stroke, 34,* 1346–1352.

Warrington, S.J., Padgham, C., & Lader, M. (1989). The cardiovascular effects of antidepressants. *Psychological Medicine Monographs Supplement, 16,* 1–40.

Wolpe, J. (1982). *The practice of behavior therapy* (3rd ed.). New York: Pergamon Press.

Woollard, J., Beilin, L., Lord, T., Puddey, I., MacAdam, D., & Rouse, I. (1995). A controlled trial of nurse counselling on lifestyle change for hypertensives treated in general practice: Preliminary results. *Clinical and Experimental Pharmacology and Physiology, 22,* 466–468.

Yusuf, S., Hawken, S., Ounpuu, S., Dans, T., Avezum, A., Lanas, F. et al. (2004). Effect of potentially modifiable risk factors associated with myocardial infarction in 52 countries (the INTERHEART study): Case-control study. *Lancet, 364,* 937–952.

8

Appendix: Tools and Resources

8.1 Overview

This appendix includes some of the forms that we have developed for use by cardiac patients and by their cognitive behavior therapists. We have used them in several clinical trials at the Behavioral Medicine Center at Washington University School of Medicine in St. Louis, and we have found them to be clinically useful adjuncts to the standard forms that are often used in CBT for depression, anxiety, or other problems.

8.2 Dysfunctional Attitudes About Health

This is a 20-item supplement to the widely-used Dysfunctional Attitudes Scale (DAS). The DAS was originally developed by Weissman and Beck to assess dysfunctional attitudes that are often associated with depression. David Burns provides an expanded version of the DAS in his classic cognitive-behavioral self-help manual, *Feeling Good.* Our supplement to Burns's version of the DAS includes items pertaining to poor health or its consequences. They reflect the most common dysfunctional attitudes about health that we encounter in working with depressed or anxious cardiac patients. The items can be summed the same way as the standard DAS to yield a total "dysfunctional attitudes about health" score. High scores on this scale suggest that dysfunctional attitudes about health may be important contributors to the patient's distress, and that they should be considered possible targets of the cognitive-behavioral intervention for this patient. The scale can then be used to assess treatment-related improvements in attitudes toward health.

8.3 Techniques for Overcoming Depression

We usually administer this scale sometime soon after the first treatment session, when the therapeutic relationship has begun to strengthen and the patient has been introduced to the cognitive-behavioral intervention. Completing the scale at this point alerts the patient to the fact that there are numerous techniques for overcoming depression, including some that he or she may have never tried. We administer it again at the end of active treatment, and in some cases, in the middle of treatment. When patients compare their ratings to the ones they provided at the beginning of treatment, they are often pleasantly surprised to find how many more of these techniques they are utilizing than they were before. In many cases, this increases the patient's self-efficacy for overcoming his or her depression.

8.4   CBT Problem List

Most depressed, anxious, or otherwise distressed cardiac patients have more problems than they know how to cope with. Treatment is ineffective if it focuses on problems that are either intractable or irrelevant to the goals of the intervention, or if it addresses too many problems at the same time. Consequently, identification and prioritization of treatment targets is an essential part of treatment planning. We use the Problem List (PLIST) at several points in treatment. Within the first two sessions, we ask the patient to complete a PLIST and to rank the problems according to his or her own priorities. We then discuss the pros and cons of focusing on these particular problems, and in some cases, we identify other problems that might be as important or more important to address. Typically, the overarching problem(s) that brought the patient into therapy, such as depression or anxiety, are omitted from the patient's initial list. The patient and therapist then work towards agreement on a *collaborative* PLIST and prioritize the problems according to what is likely to be most helpful. The collaborative list is then reviewed every few sessions and revised as needed. The rating scales attached to each problem provide the therapist with useful information about the patient's expectancies and motivation. In addition, the ratings are usually informative for the patients themselves.

8.5   CBT Treatment Planning Table for Cardiac Patients

This form is used to encourage therapists to think systematically about the targets of change they are planning to address, and the mediators of change they are planning to use to treat these target problems. It is also used to document the components of CBT that are delivered in each session and the problem domains that were addressed. For example, one of our patients was extremely anxious about the possibility that he might have a heart attack. The therapist planned a three-pronged intervention for this problem, involving modification of distorted, anxiogenic automatic thoughts; stress management; and increasing the patient's knowledge about his heart disease and how to manage it. However, it would have been counterproductive and overwhelming to cover all of these approaches in a single session. The therapist entered check marks in rows 3, 6, and 10 in the Heart Disease column, but she was unsure which one(s) would actually wind up on the session's collaborative agenda. The patient and she decided to focus initially on distressing cognitions and to defer the other approaches until later. After the session, she circled the checkmark in the 3rd row to indicate that this mediator of change was utilized in the session to address one of the key problems that the patient was having in coping with his heart disease.

Dysfunctional Attitudes About Health
(Supplement to the Dysfunctional Attitudes Scale)

#	Attitude	Agree strongly	Agree slightly	Neutral	Disagree slightly	Disagree very much
36	If I don't take care of myself, I deserve to get sick.	−2	−1	0	1	2
37	People would feel sorry for me if they knew I were ill.	−2	−1	0	1	2
38	I should be able to do the things I used to do when I was healthier.	−2	−1	0	1	2
39	Being ill makes a person hard to be with.	−2	−1	0	1	2
40	People will resent it if they have to take care of me.	−2	−1	0	1	2
41	It's unfair for me to have health problems.	−2	−1	0	1	2
42	I should be able to take care of other people who need help even when I'm not feeling well myself.	−2	−1	0	1	2
43	Other people would mind taking care of me, even if I wouldn't mind taking care of them.	−2	−1	0	1	2
44	I can't be happy unless I'm in good health.	−2	−1	0	1	2
45	It's useless to try to stay healthy, because people get sick no matter what they do.	−2	−1	0	1	2
46	I can't accomplish anything if I'm sick.	−2	−1	0	1	2
47	I deserve to be healthy if I take good care of myself.	−2	−1	0	1	2
48	Because of my illness, I'm not the same person I used to be.	−2	−1	0	1	2
49	Being ill is no excuse for being a burden, even if it's only for a short time.	−2	−1	0	1	2
50	I'm not a good (husband, wife, parent, etc.) if my health prevents me from keeping up with my responsibilities.	−2	−1	0	1	2
51	Because of my health problems, I can't have any fun or do anything I want to do.	−2	−1	0	1	2
52	I have to put other people's needs first, even if doing so might hurt my own health.	−2	−1	0	1	2
53	I'm never going to get any better.	−2	−1	0	1	2
54	People won't love me if I'm not healthy.	−2	−1	0	1	2
55	I should be able to cope with my health problems without asking anyone for help.	−2	−1	0	1	2

From: J.A. Skala, K.E. Freedland, & R.M. Carney: *Heart Disease* © 2005 Hogrefe & Huber Publishers

Techniques for Overcoming Depression

Name: _____   Date: _____

Instructions: These are some of the techniques that can help people to overcome their depression. Some of them may be more helpful or more important for you than other ones are. Lately, how often have you been using these techniques?

#	Technique	Never or rarely	Some-times	Often	Very often
1	Find more or better emotional support from other people.	0	1	2	3
2	Challenge the depressing thoughts and images that run through my mind, and practice more helpful ways of thinking.	0	1	2	3
3	Challenge my depressing beliefs and attitudes, and work on replacing them with more helpful ones.	0	1	2	3
4	Challenge the negative ideas I have about myself, and work on replacing them with ideas that improve my self-esteem.	0	1	2	3
5	Figure out if I'm doing something to help or protect myself that actually makes my problems worse or makes me feel worse, and work on finding better ways to take care of myself.	0	1	2	3
6	Develop better ways to cope with the hard realities of life, especially problems that are beyond my control (like having a serious illness or losing a loved one.)	0	1	2	3
7	Review my priorities, values, or goals in life, and work to change whatever is getting in the way of having a better life.	0	1	2	3
8	Improve my ability to cope with everyday hassles & problems.	0	1	2	3
9	Work on improving my social life, spending more time with other people I enjoy, or meeting new people.	0	1	2	3
10	Get more active doing things I enjoy or get pleasure out of, such as recreational activities, hobbies, reading, travel, etc.	0	1	2	3
11	Get more active doing things that give me a sense of accomplishment or achievement, or that make me feel that I'm doing something useful, important, or helpful.	0	1	2	3
12	Actively work on solving the problems that get me down.	0	1	2	3
13	If something important is not going the way I want it to, figure out what I can do to make it go better.	0	1	2	3
14	Practice techniques for relaxing and managing stress.	0	1	2	3
15	Improve my skills for dealing with difficult social situations, such as learning how to be assertive, finding better ways to communicate, controlling my anger, etc.	0	1	2	3
16	Learn more about how to manage my health problems or how to get good health care.	0	1	2	3
17	Other:	0	1	2	3
18	Other:	0	1	2	3

From: J.A. Skala, K.E. Freedland, & R.M. Carney: *Heart Disease*   © 2005 Hogrefe & Huber Publishers

CBT Problem List

Name: _____   Date: _____

Current priority	Problem		Rating		
		Not at all	**A little**	**A lot**	**Very much**
	a. How bad (down, worried, angry, etc.) have you been feeling about this problem?	0	1	2	3
	b. How well have you been coping with it lately?	0	1	2	3
	c. How hard have you been trying to solve this problem or improve this situation?	0	1	2	3
	d. How strongly do you believe that you can overcome it?	0	1	2	3
	e. How much better do you think you will feel if you make some good progress on this?	0	1	2	3
	f. How willing are you to work on it with your therapist?	0	1	2	3
		Not at all	**A little**	**A lot**	**Very much**
	a. How bad (down, worried, angry, etc.) have you been feeling about this problem?	0	1	2	3
	b. How well have you been coping with it lately?	0	1	2	3
	c. How hard have you been trying to solve this problem or improve this situation?	0	1	2	3
	d. How strongly do you believe that you can overcome it?	0	1	2	3
	e. How much better do you think you will feel if you make some good progress on this?	0	1	2	3
	f. How willing are you to work on it with your therapist?	0	1	2	3
		Not at all	**A little**	**A lot**	**Very much**
	a. How bad (down, worried, angry, etc.) have you been feeling about this problem?	0	1	2	3
	b. How well have you been coping with it lately?	0	1	2	3
	c. How hard have you been trying to solve this problem or improve this situation?	0	1	2	3
	d. How strongly do you believe that you can overcome it?	0	1	2	3
	e. How much better do you think you will feel if you make some good progress on this?	0	1	2	3
	f. How willing are you to work on it with your therapist?	0	1	2	3

From: J.A. Skala, K.E. Freedland, & R.M. Carney: *Heart Disease*   © 2005 Hogrefe & Huber Publishers

Cognitive Therapy for Cardiac Patients
Treatment Planning Table

Patient: _____ Date: _____

Instructions: Use this grid for planning treatment sessions. Refer to the current problem list to identify potential targets of change. For each target area that you want to include on the session agenda, place a check mark in the row(s) corresponding to the mediators of change that you think are likely to be especially useful in this case. After the session, circle any items that worked well during the session and cross out ones that turned out to be ineffective or counterproductive.

		Targets of change								
		Distress				Stressors				
#	Mediators of change	Depres-sion Grief Loss	Anxiety	Anger Hos-tility	Lone-liness LPSS	Heart Dz	Other Dz	Inter-per-sonal conflict	Work or $	Other
1	Use therapeutic relationship to provide emotional support, encouragement, etc.									
2	Normalize, conceptualize, explain patient's problems (e.g., teach about depression); provide rationale for treatment; set Tx goals									
3	Identify, challenge, change automatic thoughts and cognitive distortions									
4	Identify, challenge, change dysfunctional attitudes, beliefs, rules, schemas, and/or compensatory strategies									
5	Improve ability to: cope with harsh realities; adjust to losses, disappointments, setbacks; change priorities, values, goals to adapt to difficult circumstances									
6	Develop cognitive-behavioral stress mgt skills, e.g., relaxation, positive reinterpretation, etc.									
7	Behavioral activation to increase: social, recreational, or work activities; opportunities for pleasure, mastery, social reinforcement, social support									

From: J.A. Skala, K.E. Freedland, & R.M. Carney: *Heart Disease*   © 2005 Hogrefe & Huber Publishers

| # | Mediators of change | Targets of change | | | | | | | | |
| | | Distress | | | | Stressors | | | | |
		Depression Grief Loss	Anxiety	Anger Hostility	Loneliness LPSS	Heart Dz	Other Dz	Interpersonal conflict	Work or $	Other
8	Improve: problem-solving or decision-making skills; ability to assess and change own role in problematic interpersonal situations; ability to plan ahead									
9	Improve assertiveness, communication, anger mgt, or other interpersonal skills									
10	Increase knowledge of health, health care; improve ability to cope with or manage illness									
11	Develop self-therapy, relapse-prevention skills and plan for further intervention if needed									
12	Other:									

From: J.A. Skala, K.E. Freedland, & R.M. Carney: *Heart Disease*   © 2005 Hogrefe & Huber Publishers

Problem and Pathological Gambling

In the series: Advances in Psychotherapy – Evidence-Based Practice

James P. Whelan, Andrew W. Meyers

Over the past 30 years there has been a dramatic increase in the availability of convenient and legal gambling opportunities. Most people can reach a casino in a matter of a few hours, lottery tickets in minutes, or an online gaming site in seconds. Accompanying this proliferation of gambling is a growing understanding that between 5% and 9% of adults experience significant to severe problems due to their gambling activities. These problems have become a real health concern, with substantial costs to individuals, families, and communities.

The objective of this book is to provide the clinician – or graduate student – with essential information about problem and pathological gambling. After placing this behavioral addiction and its co-occurring difficulties in perspective, by describing its proliferation, the associated costs, and diagnostic criteria and definitions, the authors present detailed information on a strategy to assess and treat gambling problems in an outpatient setting.

They go on to provide clear and easy-to-follow intervention guidelines, including homework assignments, for a brief and cost-efficient cognitive behavioral approach to problem gambling, involving stepped care and guided self-change. Means of countering problems and barriers to change and vivid case vignettes round off this thorough, but compact guide for clinicians.

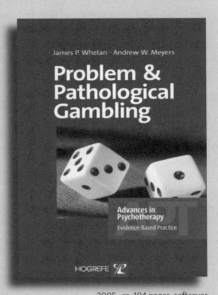

James P. Whelan · Andrew W. Meyers

Problem & Pathological Gambling

Advances in Psychotherapy
Evidence-Based Practice

HOGREFE

2005, ca. 104 pages, softcover
ISBN: 0-88937-312-4 , US $ / € 24.95
Standing order price US $ / € 19.95
(minimum 4 successive vols.)
*Special rates for members of the Society of Clinical Psychology (APA D12) - Single volume: US $19.95
- Standing order: US $17.95 per volume
(please supply membership # when ordering)

Table of Contents

1. Description: Terminology and Definitions • Epidemiology • Course and Prognosis • Differential Diagnosis • Comorbidities • Diagnostic Procedures and Documentation
2. Theories and Models of the Disorder
3. Diagnosis and Treatment Indications
4. Treatment: Methods of Treatment • Mechanisms of Action • Efficacy and Prognosis • Variations and Combinations of Methods • Problems and Barriers to Change
5. Case Vignette
6. Further Reading
7. References
8. Appendix: Tools and Resources

Order online at: **www.hhpub.com**

HOGREFE

Bipolar Disorder

In the series: Advances in Psychotherapy – Evidence-Based Practice

Rober P. Reiser, Larry W. Thompson

The past 10 years have seen a dramatic increase of interest in psychosocial treatments of bipolar disorder. There is now substantial empirical evidence suggesting the effectiveness of such treatments. However, this accumulated information has not yet been transferred into clinical practice in many settings.

Help is now at hand. This compact volume brings to the practitioner a comprehensive, evidence-based approach to the treatment of bipolar disorder that is practical, easily accessible, and can be readily applied in clinical practice.

This practitioner's guide begins by describing the main features of bipolar disorder and considerations for differential diagnosis based on DSM-IV and ICD-10 criteria. Following this, current theories and models are described, along with decision trees for evaluating the best treatment options. The volume then guides the reader through a systematic, integrated approach to treatment, based on the best of recent research. The authors describe a structured directive therapy that is also collaborative and client centered. Special considerations, including managing suicide risk, substance misuse, and medication nonadherence, are addressed. The volume is rounded off by the inclusion of clinically oriented tools and sample forms.

Robert P. Reiser · Larry W. Thompson

Bipolar Disorder

Advances in Psychotherapy
Evidence-Based Practice

HOGREFE

2005, 120 pages, softcover
ISBN: 0-88937-310-8 , US $ / € 24.95
Standing order price US $ / € 19.95
(minimum 4 successive vols.)
*Special rates for members of the Society of Clinical Psychology (APA D12) - Single volume: US $19.95
- Standing order: US $17.95 per volume
(please supply membership # when ordering)

Table of Contents

1. Description: Terminology • Definition • Epidemiology • Course and Prognosis • Differential Diagnosis • Comorbidities • Diagnostic Procedures and Documentation
2. Theories and Models of the Disorder
3. Diagnosis and Treatment Indications
4. Treatment: Methods of Treatment • Mechanisms of Action • Efficacy and Prognosis • Variations and Combinations of Methods • Problems in Carrying out the Treatment
5. Further Reading
6. References
7. Appendices: Tools and Resources

Order online at: **www.hhpub.com**

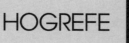

Childhood Maltreatment

In the series: Advances in Psychotherapy – Evidence-Based Practice

Christine Wekerle, Alec L. Miller, David A. Wolfe, Carrie B. Spindel

The serious consequences of child abuse or maltreatment are among the most challenging things therapists encounter. There has in recent years been a surge of interest, and of both basic and clinical research, concerning early traumatization. This volume in the series *Advances in Psychotherapy* integrates results from the latest research showing the importance of early traumatization, into a compact and practical guide for practitioners. Advances in biological knowledge have highlighted the potential chronicity of effects of childhood maltreatment, demonstrating particular life challenges in managing emotions, forming and maintaining healthy relationships, healthy coping, and holding a positive outlook of oneself. Despite the resiliency of many maltreated children, adolescent and young adult well-being is often compromised. This text first overviews our current knowledge of the effects of childhood maltreatment on psychiatric and psychological health, then provides diagnostic guidance, and subsequently goes on to profile promising and effective evidence-based interventions. Consistent with the discussions of treatment, prevention programming that is multi-targeted at issues for maltreated individuals is highlighted. This text helps the practitioner or student to know what to look for, what questions need to be asked, how to handle the sensitive ethical implications, and what are promising avenues for effective coping.

2005, ca. 104 pages, softcover
ISBN: 0-88937-314-0 , US $ / € 24.95
Standing order price US $ / € 19.95
(minimum 4 successive vols.)
*Special rates for members of the Society of Clinical Psychology (APA D12) - Single volume: US $19.95
- Standing order: US $17.95 per volume
(please supply membership # when ordering)

Table of Contents
1. Description: Terminology • Definitions • Epidemiology • Course and Prognosis • Differential Diagnosis • Comorbidities • Diagnostic Procedures and Documentation
2. Theories and Models of the Disorder
3. Diagnosis and Treatment Indications
4. Treatment: Methods of Treatment • Mechanisms of Action • Efficacy and Prognosis • Variations and Combinations of Methods • Problems and Barriers to Change
5. Case Vignette
6. Further Reading
7. References
8. Appendix: Tools and Resources

Order online at: **www.hhpub.com**

Advances in Psychotherapy – Evidence-Based Practice

Developed and edited in consultation with the Society of Clinical Psychology (APA Division 12).

Pricing / Standing Order Terms

Regular Prices: Single-volume – $24.95; Series Standing Order – $19.95
APA D12 member prices: Single-volume – $19.95; Series Standing Order – $17.95
With a Series Standing Order you will automatically be sent each new volume upon its release. After a minimum of 4 successive volumes, the Series Standing Order can be cancelled at any time. If you wish to pay by credit card, we will hold the details on file but your card will only be charged when a new volume actually ships.

Order Form (please check a box)

[ ] I would like to place a Standing Order for the series at the special price of US $ / €19.95 per volume, starting with volume no. ....

[ ] I am a D12 Member and would like to place a Standing Order for the series at the special D12 Member Price of US $ / € 17.95 per volume, starting with volume no. ......
My APA D12 membership no. is:

[ ] I would like to order the following single volumes at the regular price of US $ / € 24.95 per volume.

[ ] I am a D12 Member and would like to order the following single volumes at the special D12 Member Price of US $ / € 24.95 per volume.
My APA D12 membership no. is:

Qty.	Author / Title / ISBN	Price	Total
		Subtotal	

WA residents add 8.8% sales tax; Canadians 7% GST

Shipping & handling:
USA — US $6.00 per volume (multiple copies: US $1.25 for each further copy)
Canada — US $8.00 per volume (multiple copies: US $2.00 for each further copy)
South America: — US $10.00 per volume (multiple copies: US $2.00 for each further copy)
Europe: — € 6.00 per volume (multiple copies: € 1.25 for each further copy)
Rest of the World: — € 8.00 per volume (multiple copies: € 1.50 for each further copy)

Total

[ ] Check enclosed   [ ] Please bill me   [ ] Charge my: [ ] VISA   [ ] MC   [ ] AmEx
Card # _____   CVV2/CVC2/CID # _____   Exp date _____

Signature _____

Shipping address (please include phone & fax) _____
_____
_____
_____

Order online at: **www.hhpub.com**

Hogrefe & Huber Publishers • 30 Amberwood Parkway · Ashland, OH 44805 • Tel: (800) 228-3749 · Fax: (419) 281-6883
Hogrefe & Huber Publishers, Rohnsweg 25 • D-37085 Göttingen, Germany, Tel: +49 551 49609-0, Fax: +49 551 49609-88
E-Mail: custserv@hogrefe.com